Other Titles of Interest

HOW TO GET YOUR
ELECTRONIC PROJECTS WORKING

by
R. A. Penfold

BERNARD BABANI (publishing) LTD
THE GRAMPIANS
SHEPHERDS BUSH ROAD
LONDON W6 7NF
ENGLAND

PLEASE NOTE

© 1982 BERNARD BABANI (publishing) LTD

First Published — October 1982
Reprinted — May 1988
Reprinted — April 1990
Reprinted — October 1992

British Library Cataloguing in Publication Data
Penfold, R. A.
    How to get your electronic projects working.
    — (BP110)
    1: Electronic apparatus and appliances — Maintenance
    and repair — Amateurs' manuals
    I. Title
    621.381   TK9965

ISBN 0 85934 085 6

Printed and bound in Great Britain by Cox & Wyman Ltd, Reading

Preface

Although modern electronic constructional methods have reduced the risk of errors when building electronic projects, and most electronic components these days are highly reliable and few "duds" are on sale, sooner or later most constructors build a project that fails to work first time. Usually the problem can be traced to a simple wiring error or something of this nature, but there is always the occasional awkward project which fails to work properly for no apparent reason.

In a publication such as this there is obviously only a limited amount of space available, and it would be quite impractical to give individual servicing information for every constructional project ever published, or even for a small percentage of them. Fortunately this is not really necessary, and by looking at the problem in a logical manner and proceeding accordingly it is possible to fault-find on practically any piece of electronic equipment.

The purpose of this book then, is to familiarise the reader with a few basic fault-finding techniques which should then enable him or her to locate and rectify the faults in virtually any electronic project that refuses to operate properly after completion. Effective fault-finding does require a certain amount of test equipment, but an ordinary digital or analogue multimeter is often all that is required. There are occasions when additional test equipment is essential, and many occasions when one or two simple items of test gear can greatly speed up the fault-finding process, but are admittedly not essential. A few inexpensive and simple, but nevertheless very useful items of test equipment are described in this book, plus detailed notes on their use, of course.

Little knowledge of electronics is assumed, and this book should be helpful to those who have only a small amount of electronics construction experience as well as those who have acquired some practical and technical knowledge of the subject.

R. A. Penfold

CONTENTS

Chapter 1

MECHANICAL FAULTS

Having been confronted with a substantial number of newly constructed, non-functioning project over a period of years (including a number not constructed by myself), problems such as faulty components, design faults, and other forms of purely electronic fault seem to be in the minority. The vast majority of faults seem to be what could be broadly termed mechanical faults, by which I mean things such as short circuits between printed circuit tracks, "dry" soldered joints, and components connected incorrectly.

Because of this it is a fortunate fact that most newly built projects which fail to work are easily corrected using little or no test gear, and little or no technical know-how is required either. On the other hand it is an unfortunate fact that quite simple faults can take quite a long time to track down, especially when dealing with a large project where thorough inspection and checking of the unit for such things as wiring errors and accidental short circuits can take a great deal of time merely because of the large number of individual checks that are required.

Of course, every project should be thoroughly and carefully checked for errors at least once, and preferably two or three times before it is switched on and tried out. This is especially important with mains powered projects, or those powered from a low impedance battery supply such as a car battery or NiCad cells, where errors could easily cause expensive damage to the components and could even be dangerous.

Being realistic about it, most constructors are eager to try out a new project and most electronic projects probably receive a minimal amount of checking before they are tried out. Beginners tend to be a little hesitant before turning on a new project, but as constructors' experience increases they tend to become more confident and do less initial checking. A case of "familiarity breeding contempt" perhaps. In most cases a lack of initial checking is unlikely to cause expensive damage or prove to be dangerous, but is not really something to be recommended! It is advisable to at least give the wiring a quick visual check for any obvious errors, and also make quite sure that any preset components are at the right initial settings before switching on. The text of the book or magazine article concerned should make it quite clear if it is important for any presets to be at certain initial settings, and there are cases where a grossly incorrect setting could cause damage to the circuit at switch-on. For example, discrete class B power amplifiers usually have a preset resistor to set the appropriate quiescent bias current through the output stage, and this is normally set for zero bias current at first, and then advanced to the correct setting once the circuit is operating. With the preset at the wrong end of its adjustment range there is likely to be a very high current flow through the output devices at switch-on, and this could easily lead to their rapid destruction!

Therefore you should always read any initial setting up instructions and follow them exactly, and give the wiring at least a quick check before switching the unit on.

Provided you have some idea of the expected current consumption of the circuit, it is a good idea to use a multimeter switched to a suitable current range to check that the supply current is approximately correct at switch-on. Do not worry if the reading is briefly much higher than expected at switch-on. Provided it rapidly falls back to the correct level it is unlikely that this is indicative of a malfunction, and is almost certainly just due to supply decoupling capacitors in the circuit taking up their initial charge.

If the current consumption obtained is considerably in error, say less than half or more than double the expected figure, this almost certainly is indicative of a fault and you should switch the unit off at once. If you are not using a multimeter to monitor the current consumption, it will probably be immediately obvious if the circuit is not functioning properly, and you should switch off the power as soon as it becomes apparent that all is not well with the unit. Leaving the unit switched on could possibly result in damage to components, especially in cases where the current consumption is much higher than it should be.

Mechanical Checking

Having discovered that the project does not work the first job is to thoroughly check that all the wiring is correct, with the emphasis on thoroughness. If the project is mains powered it should be unplugged from the mains supply so that it can be checked without any danger of a serious electric shock being received.

When looking for errors it is important to check anything that could be the cause of the fault, and not to just check that components are correctly placed on the circuit board, and that the controls, sockets, etc. are correctly wired up. Check that integrated circuits are fitted onto the board with the correct orientation, that polarised capacitors such as electrolytic and tantalum capacitors are connected with the right polarity, and that other components such as diodes and transistors are connected correctly. If you are using a type of transistor that you are not familiar with be sure to study the base leadout diagram for the device concerned and then check the device is fitted in place correctly.

It is suprisingly easy to misread resistor colour codes even if you are familiar with these components and the coding. The coding for a 220 ohm component (red, red, brown) is easily confused with that for a 1.2k resistor (brown, red, red) for example, and some resistors have coloured bands that are rather ambiguous. For instance, I have come across resistors having red colour coding bands that were easily confused for brown bands, and others having violet coding bands that were so dark as to appear to be black under normal lighting conditions. It is therefore advisable to take a close look at any resistor that looks at all doubtful, and check the resistance using an ohm-meter if necessary. However, when measuring the resistance of a component that is in-circuit remember that other components in the circuit can affect the reading obtained, and can result in a low reading being produced. Thus, unless you are using an in-circuit resistance meter, temporarily desolder one leadout wire of the resistor before measuring its value.

Apart from wiring errors and other simple mistakes in construction probably the most common cause of failure in new projects is accidental short circuits between copper tracks on the underside of the printed circuit board caused by small blobs of excess solder. As time goes by the layouts of circuit boards seem to become more and more crowded, and as the printed circuit tracks become more closely spaced the risk of such accidental short circuits becomes increasingly great. It is an unfortunate fact that the higher the density of a board the more difficult it becomes to visually trace a solder blob causing a short circuit. This is simply because the offending solder blob may be so small as to be virtually impossible to see with the naked eye.

Another problem when trying to visually trace a minute solder blob is that it may not actually be visible at all, and may be covered over by excess flux from the solder. Before giving a board a visual inspection for solder blobs it is therefore necessary to clean off any excess flux, and it is virtually certain that there will in fact be plenty of this to remove from the board.

There are special aerosol solvents that can be used when cleaning flux from printed circuit boards, but an inexpensive and popular alternative is to use a rag moistened with methylated spirit. However, bear in mind tha methylated spirit is highly inflammable and should not be used near a naked flame.

As mentioned above, the solder blobs can be very small and difficult to see with the naked eye. A magnifier of some kind is therefore very useful when visually checking boards for short circuits. Also, bear in mind that although short circuits between copper tracks are most often caused by blobs of solder near to soldered joints or between soldered joints, it does sometimes happen that a thin trail of solder can be left across printed circuit tracks, and these can be quite difficult to spot. This is particularly the case when dealing with a printed circuit board having thin tracks that are tinned with solder since the solder trail can be almost indistinguishable from a proper printed circuit track. When dealing with boards of this type it might be worthwhile checking the board against the printed circuit track diagram to ensure that there are no extra tracks! If you are using a home-constructed printed circuit board this should be checked against the track diagram to make sure that no errors have been made when applying the

4

etch resist. With modern complex board it is very easy to carelessly lay a track between the wrong two places on the board, and it is even easier to accidentally miss out a short piece of track.

The first places to look for solder bridges are any points on the board where there is a high density of solder joints, and this usually means the places on the board where integrated circuits are situated, and there is often an increase in density in the region of transistors as well. When using stripboard I have often found that solder bridges are easily formed where there are connections close together at the edges of the board, and these can be difficult to see if there is only a very thin solder bridge right at the edge of the board. Therefore special attention should be payed to the edges of stripboards. A technique that is sometimes successful with stripboards where it seems likely that a solder bridge is present, but it cannot be seen, is to run the point of a modelling knife hard down between each set of copper tracks two or three times so that any very thin solder bridges are broken. However, take care not to cut anything other than any solder bridges that are present, and keep the hand that is holding the board well out of the way of the knife blade.

Dry Joints

Dry joints were once a common fault, but modern solders and component leads have reduced dry joints to something of a rarity. Components leadouts normally have a plating that minimises oxidation, and the fluxes in modern solder are first rate at removing oxidised layers and getting the solder to flow nicely over the surfaces to be joined. You would probably find it hard to produce a dry joint even if you tried to!

Despite this, dry joints can occur from time to time if you are not careful. The way in which this usually happens is the soldering iron is left for some time during construction with a substantial amount of solder left on the bit. During this period of time any flux in the solder completely burns away, and the solder begins to oxidise and may deteriorate considerably. When the next soldered joint is made after this a small amount of fresh solder is introduced, but the joint is mainly formed by the solder from the bit.

This gives two problems. Firstly there is the absence of sufficient flux to make the solder flow over the joined surfaces properly, and instead of a proper joint as shown in Figure 1(a) being obtained, a joint such as that shown in Figure 1(b) is produced. The solder is not in proper contact with the printed circuit track, and may not even be in good electrical contact with the leadout wire. The second problem is that even if the solder does appear to flow over the leadout wire and copper track properly, there may not actually be a good electrical connection. It can sometimes happen that even where a joint is very strong mechanically there is not a good electrical connection, and this problem is presumably due to oxidised layers tending to insulate the leadout wire or the copper track from the solder.

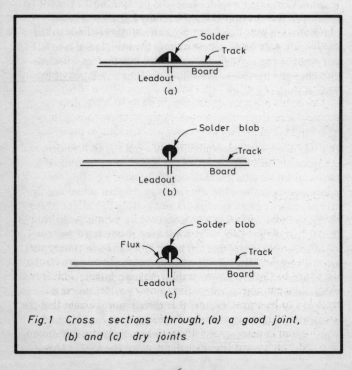

Fig.1 Cross sections through, (a) a good joint,
(b) and (c) dry joints

Another problem that can arise is a purely mechanical one. Even if a good electrical connection is present, the fact that the solder has oxidised to some extent normally weakens it mechanically, and it also seems to solidify more slowly so that any slight movement during the solidification process is more likely to cause fractures in the solder and a mechanically weak joint.

It does sometimes happen that even using fresh solder applied to the joint in the correct manner a dry joint is still produced, and this occurs when soldering a leadout wire or copper track that is severely corroded so that the flux cannot penetrate the corrosion. The result is usually a joint of the type shown in Figure 1(c), and although this may be quite strong mechanically, a layer of flux usually insulates the leadout wire and the solder from the copper track.

Of course, it is better to avoid dry joints than to rectify them, and this can be achieved by cleaning solder from the bit of a soldering iron which has been standing switched on but unused for some time, and retinning the bit just before starting to reuse the iron. Any leadout wire or copper track that shows obvious signs of severe corrosion or is simply very dirty should be cleaned prior to making a connection.

Dry joints are not usually too difficult to track down visually since the sort of mountain shape of a proper joint is replaced by a globular appearance if a dry joint is present. Another tell-tail sign is rather dull looking oxidised solder instead of the normal very shiny solder.

Broken Tracks

Broken printed circuit board tracks are by no means a common problem, and normally only occur when servicing equipment and it becomes necessary to remove and replace a component. This can weaken the adhesive which bonds the copper track to the board so that the tracks tend to lift and break. This is not likely to occur when constructing a new project unless an error has to be corrected, and it is then almost certain that the damage to the board will be self evident.

What can happen, especially with home-constructed boards, is that the etch resist becomes slightly damaged prior to etching of the board, or perhaps at some point the etch resist is inadequate so that the completed board has a broken track at some point.

Unless the break in the track is very small indeed it should be easy to spot it, and it will probably be found that the break can simply be soldered over. If necessary a small link wire can be soldered across the break, and another alternative is to use one of the conductive paints that are available and which can be used to simply paint in any missing pieces of track. These paints are most useful where a fairly long piece of track has to be added, but they are normally silver based and are consequently extremely expensive (although only a very small bottle of paint is sufficient for a large number of repairs).

Continuity Tester

Apart from making visual checks for short circuits or breaks in wiring it is of course possible to check for them electronically, and this method will often find faults that are not readily apparent from a visual inspection of the project. The disadvantage of this method is that it can take a great deal of time to thoroughly check over even a quite small piece of equipment, and for this reason it is recommended that a visual check of faulty equipment should always be made first.

A continuity tester can simply be a multimeter switched to a fairly low ohms range (say a range having a maximum reading of around 10k). It is not advisable to use a high resistance range as there is then the possibility of a fairly substantial resistance across the test prods not registering as such on the meter, and misleading results could thus be obtained. A very low resistance range is likely to be satisfactory, but some multimeters pass quite a high current through the test prods on the lowest resistance range, and this does give a slight risk of damage to delicate components in the circuit under investigation.

In use a continuity tester is very easy to use, and it is simply a matter of placing the test prods on (say) two adjacent copper tracks of a stripboard to ensure that there is no short circuit between them, or between a leadout wire and a copper track to ensure that they are in fact in electrical connection.

One slight problem that can arise is that of a low resistance

8

between copper tracks giving the impression that there is a short circuit present. You cannot, therefore, automatically assume that a short circuit caused by a solder blob is present if a low resistance is indicated by the meter, and must check that there is not a component connected between the tracks that would provide a low resistance path. Bear in mind that components other than resistors can provide a low resistance path. Inductors and transformers provide low resistances through their windings, for example.

Confusing results can also be produced by semiconductor junctions, and this includes junctions in transistors and integrated circuits, and not just straight forward diode junctions. For instance, the base emitter junction of a transistor is effectively a silicon diode (with the emitter as the cathode and the base as the anode). Whether or not misleading results are obtained depends entirely on the type of continuity tester in use, and some digital multimeters when switched to an ohms range use a test voltage that is too low to forward bias a silicon diode to the point where it conducts significantly. With this type of meter there is no problem, and applying the test prods to a silicon diode with either polarity will produce an open circuit indication from the meter (although this type of meter does have the slight disadvantage of being unsuitable for diode checking as a consequence of this).

Most digital multimeters will give a fairly high resistance reading when connected so that the junction is forward biased, and are thus unlikely to give misleading results. The circuits used in analogue multimeters when used to measure resistance tend to give a less clear indication of a diode junction, but the reading obtained in the forward direction is always significantly less than full scale, and with care mistakes should be avoided.

There have been quite a number of continuity tester designs for the home-constructor in recent years, and some of these are capable of differentiating between a diode junction and a genuine short circuit, but the majority are very simple designs that are not. This makes it necessary to be very cautious when using one of these devices since it is quite possible that a short circuit will be indicated where none exists, or even that there is no dry joint or broken track where one does in fact exist. With these simple testers it is a good idea to reverse the test prods if a short circuit is indicated, and if it is actually a diode junction rather than a short circuit that is present an open circuit will be indicated when the prods are reversed. Or to be more accurate, an open circuit may be indicated when the test prods are reversed. There is always the possibility of there being two junctions of opposite polarity across the two tracks, and erroneous results being obtained in consequence.

Practical Design

The best way of avoiding erroneous results is to use a continuity tester that can differentiate between a semiconductor junction and a genuine short circuit, and a tester of this type can be very simple and inexpensive to build. A practical design for a continuity tester of this type is shown in the circuit diagram of Figure 2.

The unit is intended to be built as a small hand held probe, and a tri-colour LED indicator shows whether or not there is continuity between the probe tip and the test prod. For those who are not familiar with tri-colour LEDs it should perhaps be explained that they are basically just a red LED and a green LED in the same encapsulation, and having three leadout wires (either the two anode leads or the two cathode leads have a common leadout wire). If only the red or green LED is switched on, then the LED glows red or green as appropriate. However, due to a diffusion screen at the front of the component a yellow or orange output is produced if both LEDs are switched on simultaneously. The exact colour produced depends on the relative strengths of the red and green sections of the LED.

The tricolour LED is used to indicate the following states:

Red:	Open circuit
Yellow:	Semiconductor junction (forward biased)
Green:	Short circuit (or very low resistance).

It is possible for a resistance to give a yellow indication from the unit, but only a limited range of resistances (from around 20 to 100 ohms) will do this, and this is not of great practical importance. The main purpose of the unit is to indicate whether there is a very low impedance between the test prods, a very high impedance, or something between the two extremes. This gives the user a little more information than a simple

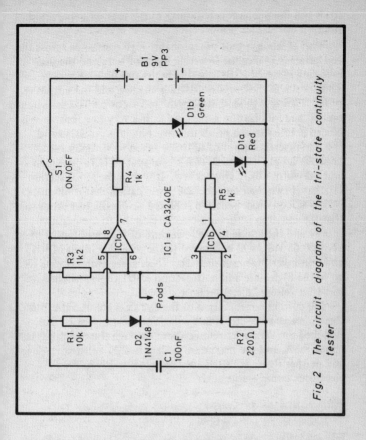

Fig. 2 The circuit diagram of the tri-state continuity tester

continuity tester of the conventional type, and with experience this can help to diagnose faults more quickly and reliably.

Operation of the circuit is quite straight forward, and the unit is based on a CA3240E dual operational amplifier which is actually used here as a dual voltage comparator. Each operational amplifier drives one section of tri-colour LED indicator D1 via a current limiting resistor (R4 and R5). R1, D2 and R2 form a potential divider circuit which produces a bias potential of only around 200mV at the junction of D2 and R2, and approximately 850mV at the junction of R1 and D2. The lower bias voltage is applied to the inverting input of

11

IC1b and the higher one is applied to the non-inverting input of IC1a.

With an open circuit or reasonably high resistance across the test prods R3 takes the inverting input of IC1a and the non-inverting input of IC1b to virtually the full positive supply rail. This results in the output of IC1a going low and the output of IC1b going high so that only the red section of D1 is switched on and a red indication is produced. If a very low resistance is placed across the test prods the inverting input of IC1a and the non-inverting input of IC1b are taken to virtually the negative supply voltage so that the output of IC1a goes high and the output of IC1b goes low. It is then the green section D1 that is switched on and a green indication that is obtained.

If a silicon diode junction is placed across the test prods so that the junction is forward biased (cathode to the negative supply and the anode to the lower end of R3), a potential of about 0.65 volts will be applied to the inverting input of IC1a and non-inverting input of IC1b. This causes both outputs to go to the high state and both section of D1 to be switched on so that a yellow indication is produced.

The current consumption of the circuit is about 5mA, but this increases to about 10mA when both sections of D1 are switched on. The maximum current through the test prods is about 8mA, and the maximum voltage is only a little over 9 volts, and neither figure is sufficiently high to put any normal electronic components at risk.

Components for Tri-State Continuity Tester (Figure 2)
Resistors, all 1/3 watt 5%

R1	10k	R2	220 ohms
R3	1k2	R4	1k
R5	1k		

Capacitor
C1   100nF polyester
Semiconductors
IC1   CA3240E
D1   Tri-colour (common cathode) LED
D2   1N4148
Switch
S1   SPST miniature toggle type

Miscellaneous

0.1in matrix stripboard
PP3 size 9 volt battery and connector to suit
Test prods and leads
Small plastic case
Wire, solder, etc.

Construction

A suitable component layout for the circuit using a 0.1in
matrix stripboard having 13 holes by 12 copper strips is shown
in Figure 3. The mounting holes in the board are 3.3mm in

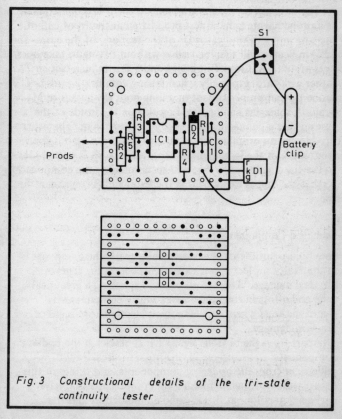

Fig. 3   Constructional   details   of   the   tri-state
continuity   tester

13

diameter and accept 6BA or M3 fixings. Do not overlook the three breaks in the copper strips.

IC1 is a MOS device and is therefore susceptible to damage by high static voltages, and the usual MOS device handling precautions should be taken. As this device is not one of the cheapest it is probably worthwhile fitting it in a socket. If a socket is not used the device should be soldered into circuit using a soldering iron having an earthed bit. In either case it should be handled as little as possible once removed from its protective packaging, and it should not be fitted into place until the other components and link wires have been fitted onto the board.

The unit will be most convenient to use if it is constructed as a probe having a metal test prod fitted at the front end of the case and LED indicator D1 at the rear end of the case. The LED indicator will then be visible without having to take ones eyes away from the circuit board under test (which can be rather awkward, especially when testing complex boards). The probe tip can simply consist of a long bolt, say an M3 or M4 type. A soldertag can be fitted on this on the inside of the case so that a connection can easily be made to it. The other prod is just an ordinary test prod, and these can be obtained from some of the larger component retailers. It is a good idea to use the smallest case that will accommodate the components so that the unit is easily held in the hand and is convenient to use.

Damaged Components

One final point is that it is worthwhile giving the components in the faulty project a quick visual inspection for signs of physical damage. There is no point in spending a great deal of time and effort in tracking down a faulty component by electronic tests when the component clearly shows signs of physical damage.

Apart from the obvious signs such as cracks in the bodies of components, transformers having broken wires, leadout wires pulled out from the bodies of components, and things of this nature, it is worthwhile looking for components that have darkened in colour as this is often an indication that the component has been overheated and possibly been damaged while being soldered into circuit. It can sometimes happen that a leadout wire has broken away from a component, but this is not readily apparent because the leadout wires are held in place by the soldered joints and the body of the component has not been displaced. Gently pulling on the bodies of components will reveal any that are damaged in this way, and this may also show up any badly soldered joints or any joints that have been accidentally omitted. It seems to be printed circuit mounting polycarbonate and polyester capacitors that are most vulnerable to this form of damage, and it is a good idea to treat these components with greater than normal care.

When searching for faults always try to be methodical, and do not just search in a random fashion. First check that the correct components are in the right places with the proper orientation where this is important. Check that the point to point wiring is correct, including such things as the polarity of battery clips. Then check for short circuits between tracks, broken tracks, and dry joints, making sure that all tracks and joints are inspected and none are overlooked (if you fail to check something it is virtually certain that the fault will lie there!). Finally check that there is no obvious damage to any of the components that has gone unnoticed during construction.

Chapter 2

LINEAR CIRCUITS

If checking for mechanical faults fails to give results it obviously becomes necessary at some stage to try a different approach, and this invariably means some form of electronic testing. Those who have a reasonably comprehensive knowledge of electronics usually prefer to resort to electronic testing at a fairly early stage in the proceedings since this type of testing can often lead to fairly swift diagnosis of the fault whatever its nature. This avoids searching for a mechanical fault that may not exist, or leads to such a fault being found reasonably quickly if it is present. For those who have only limited experience of electronic circuits and theory electronic testing is likely to be much slower and difficult, and it is probably best to thoroughly check for mechanical faults before resorting to electronic tests.

Voltage Tests

The circuit diagrams for some projects show typical voltages at various points in the circuit, and these can be very helpful indeed when fault finding. If you are familiar with the components and circuitry used in the project you may well be able to estimate expected voltages in the circuit with reasonable accuracy, and this can also be very helpful.

The basic method of testing using these voltages is fairly obvious, and it is a matter of just checking actual voltages against those specified. However, there are a few points that need to be borne in mind when taking measurements, and it is also necessary to be careful when interpreting results.

Test voltages are normally specified relative to whichever of the supply rails connects to earth or chassis, and with most modern circuits this is the negative supply rail, although this is not invariably the case. With circuits having dual supply rails it is usually the central 0V rail that is earthed. With negative earth equipment you simply connect the negative test prod to the negative supply rail and take the positive test prod to the various test points. With positive earth equipment it is obviously the positive lead that connects to the positive supply rail and the negative prod which is connected to the test points. Equipment having a central earth rail and dual supplies is a little more awkward since test voltages can be either positive or negative with respect to earth. It is thus necessary to earth the negative test prod when measuring positive voltages or the positive test prod when measuring negative voltages. Digital multimeters are very convenient when testing this type of equipment since it is then merely necessary to earth the negative test prod and the multimeter's display indicates the polarity of the test voltage.

Sometimes the test voltages given on a circuit diagram are the true voltages present in the circuit, but sometimes they will be specified as voltages obtained using a multimeter of a given sensitivity (20,000 ohms per volt normally). This can be a little difficult to understand at first, but it must be remembered that when you connect a voltmeter to a circuit you are tapping off a small amount of power to activate the voltmeter. In many cases the amount of power taken from the circuit is far too small to have any effect on the circuit under test, but if there is only a very small current flowing in the part of the circuit being measured this may well not be the case.

This point is illustrated by Figure 4 which shows the bias circuit for an emitter follower buffer amplifier. The two 1 Megohm resistors would be expected to produce a bias voltage of just half the supply voltage since the output potential of a voltage divider is (R1 + R2) divided by R2, and then the supply voltage is divided by this figure. In this simple example this gives (1 + 1) divided by 1 = 2, and 10 divided by 2 = 5 volts.

In practice the input resistance of Tr1 will shunt R2 and effectively reduce the value of this component slightly, with a consequent reduction in the bias voltage. However, for the sake of this example we will ignore this factor, and assume that the input impedance of Tr1 is too high to significantly affect the bias voltage.

If the voltage present at the junction of R1 and R2 is measured with a standard 20,000 ohms per volt multimeter switched to the 10 volt range, the resistance of the multimeter

17

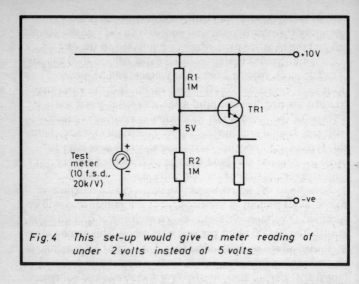

Fig. 4   This set-up would give a meter reading of under 2 volts instead of 5 volts

is placed in parallel with R2. The resistance of a multimeter is simply equal to the full scale voltage multiplied by the ohms per volt sensitivity of the instrument, and in this case is 200,000 ohms or 200k (10 volts multiplied by 20,000 ohms per volt equals 200,000 ohms). With the multimeter in circuit a potential divider action gives a bias voltage of less than one fifth of the supply voltage, or less than 2 volts instead of the correct 5 volts!

In fact the multimeter is giving an accurate reading of the voltage present at the test point, the problem is simply that the voltage is reduced when the multimeter is connected to the circuit. The test voltage is always reduced by the presence of a test meter and is never boosted.

The greater the sensitivity of the multimeter, the higher the resistance it has for a given full scale voltage value, and the lower the loading on the circuit under test. Most multimeters have a sensitivity of 20k per volt, but there are a few that have higher sensitivities, and some that have much lower sensitivities. While an insensitive multimeter is considerably better than nothing at all, it is probably worthwhile obtaining a good quality instrument of at least 20k per volt sensitivity if possible.

18

Not all test meters have sensitivities quoted in ohms per volt, and electronic types normally have an input resistance quoted in Megohms (a figure of around 10 or 11 Megohms being typical). In other words the input resistance does not change from one measuring range to another, and the sensitivity in ohms per volt changes substantially from one range to another. The advantage of an electronic multimeter is that it has a built-in amplifier which enables a very low input current to be used. This gives minimal loading on the circuit under test and is almost invariably sufficient to ensure truly accurate and reliable results. This point is demonstrated by working out the sensitivity of an electronic multimeter on (say) the 1 volt and 10 volt ranges. Assuming an input impedance of 10 Megohms this gives sensitivities of 10 Megohms and 1 Megohm per volt respectively, and this is obviously vastly superior to an ordinary multimeter.

Analogue electronic multimeters are not very common these days, but the digital multimeters that are now very popular are the modern alternative to these. While not everyone prefers digital instruments, digital multimeters are accurate, reliable, will accept inputs of either polarity (with the display indicating the polarity of the input), have high sensitivity on the DC voltage ranges, and are not easily damaged by either overloads or being dropped. One of the few disadvantages of digital multimeters is the very limited bandwidth on the AC voltage ranges, with many instruments only being suitable for use with signals up to about 1kHz in frequency. However, this is obviously sufficient for measurements at the 50 Hertz mains frequency.

If voltages on a circuit diagram are those obtained with a 20k per volt multimeter and you have a multimeter with a different sensitivity, then any voltage readings you obtain from low current parts of the circuit are likely to be significantly different to those specified on the diagram. If you are using a multimeter with a sensitivity of less than 20k per volt the readings obtained will be lower, but they will be higher if you use a meter with a sensitivity of more than 20k per volt.

If the diagram does not state that results are obtained with a multimeter of a certain sensitivity, then they are almost certain to be the true voltages (measured with a very high sensitivity meter) or even the designed voltages (obtained by calculation rather than measurement). When measuring voltages in high impedance (low current) parts of the circuit it is then likely that voltage readings obtained will be substantially lower than those indicated in the circuit diagram.

It is important to realise that voltages given on test charts or on circuit diagrams are only nominal, and that voltages in an actual (functioning) piece of equipment might well be 10% or more different to these, and multimeters do not have perfect accuracy and can therefore add another one or two percent to test voltage errors. If a test voltage is several percent in error, it is therefore quite likely that this is not indicative of an error in that particular part of the circuit. Where a major fault is present one can expect very large differences between the specified voltage and the test voltage measured, although this may not always be the case. Faults can occur that result in all the voltages in a circuit being correct under quiescent conditions, but this only happens in a minority of cases.

When a voltage that is substantially different to the expected one is discovered it may not necessarily make it clear precisely what fault condition is present, and circuits where there are a number of DC coupled stages tend to be rather difficult to check using test voltages. For example, the circuit diagram of Figure 5 shows the basic arrangement of a simple class B audio power amplifier using a Darlington Pair driver stage direct coupled to a complementary class B output stage. Normally the voltage at the emitters of output devices Tr3 and Tr4 would be approximately half the supply voltage so that a peak to peak output voltage virtually equal to the supply voltage could be produced before the output signal would be subjected to clipping and consequent distortion. Bias resistors R1 and R2 would have values that would bias the amplifier to give the appropriate output voltage at the emitters of Tr3 and Tr4.

If we assume that a voltage check shows a voltage of practically zero at the emitters of Tr3 and Tr4, there are a number of possible faults that could cause this. Obviously a short circuit between the emitter and collector terminals of Tr3, either due to a fault in the component itself or perhaps due to a short circuit between printed circuit tracks, could produce this low voltage. However, the fault could also be caused by

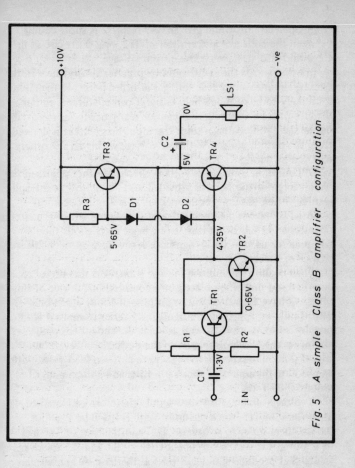

Fig. 5   A simple Class B amplifier configuration

Tr3 going open circuit, or perhaps due to a dry joint or broken printed circuit track or lead in the emitter or collector circuits of Tr3.

The fault does not actually have to be in the output stage at all. If R3 should have gone open circuit, or something has caused a lack in continuity somewhere between the upper end of R3 and the base of Tr3, the result would still be at very low output voltage from the circuit. The fault could lie even earlier in the circuit, and a fault such as R1 going closed circuit or R2 going open circuit would give similar results. A short circuit between the collector and emitter of Tr2, or a short circuit in C2 would also give a very low output voltage.

In other words the fault could be practically anywhere in the circuit, and measuring test voltages at other points in the circuit is unlikely to be of much help either. Correct voltages earlier in the circuit are something that cannot really occur with the output at the wrong voltage, since the input bias voltage is derived from the output via R1. With one voltage wrong all the others will also be wrong.

Of course, in some cases voltage checks at other points in the circuit might prove helpful provided you know how to interpret results. When checking equipment in this way it becomes essential to have some knowledge of the way in which the circuit operates and to know at least a few basic facts about the components used in the design in order to have a reasonable chance of success.

When dealing with silicon bipolar transistors it is useful to bear in mind that when biased into conduction a device of this type will have a base to emitter voltage of about 0.65 volts. This is only an approximate figure, and varies somewhat from one device to another, as well as being dependent to some extent on the base current fed to the device. However, one would normally expect a voltage quite close to 0.65 volts, with an absolute minimum of about 0.5 volts and a maximum of around 0.85 volts.

A voltage of about 1.3 volts would therefore be expected at the base of Tr1, since the emitter of Tr1 will be at about 0.65 volts in order to switch on Tr2, and the base of Tr1 will be about a further 0.65 volts above this. R1 and R2 are given values that produce about 1.3 volts at the base of Tr1 with an assumed half the supply voltage at the output (Tr3 − 4 emitters) of the amplifier. The actual voltage at the base of Tr1 may not be exactly 1.3 volts, and almost certainly will be somewhat different, but this simply results in the output voltage moving slightly away from the half supply voltage figure with a marginal loss of performance. In a practical design R1 might actually be a preset resistor so that the output voltage could be adjusted to exactly the required level.

If the output voltage was found to be about 1.3 volts, one

22

possible cause for the problem would be a short circuit from the output of the amplifier to the base of Tr1. Without the voltage drop across R1 the output will be biased to the same potential as the base of Tr1 so that both these points in the circuit go to about 1.3 volts and not half the supply rail. Of course, when making voltage checks on a circuit and two identical voltages are found, especially if one would expect the two voltages to be substantially different, it is worthwhile checking for a short circuit between the two points in question. Digital voltmeters are useful under these circumstances as they give a very precise voltage reading which makes it easier to differentiate between similar and identical voltages.

Of course, the fault may not be due to a short circuit across R1, and it may be found that there is actually a very small voltage difference across R1, with the end that connects to the base of Tr1 at the slightly lower potential. This would suggest a broken printed circuit track or dry joint in the viscinity of R2, or that this component had gone high in value. The voltage drop across R1 would then only be that produced by the high input resistance of Tr1, and this might give a voltage drop of only a few tens of millivolts.

Current Limiting

A problem that sometimes makes it difficult or impossible to take voltage readings on a circuit is that of a very high current consumption. Under these circumstances there is a very real risk of destroying components in the circuit if the unit is switched on even briefly, and damage becomes virtually certain if the supply is maintained for any length of time.

Tests without the unit switched on can be persued at first, but if these prove to be fruitless it will eventually be necessary to attempt voltage checks with the supply connected.

One way of making voltage checks under these circumstances it to use a power supply having current limiting, and with the current limit level set at whatever current the circuit would consume if it was functioning normally. An alternative is to use a resistor (of adequate power rating) in series with one of the supply leads, and the value of the resistor is chosen to give a maximum current flow that is roughly equal to the normal current consumption of the circuit under test. For example, a circuit that consumes 0.1 amps from a 20 volt power supply would require a resistor having a value of 200 ohms (20 volts divided by 0.1 amps = 200 ohms). If the calculated resistance does not coincide with a preferred value, then the nearest preferred value to the calculated figure should be chosen. The minimum acceptable wattage rating for the component is obtained by multiplying the supply voltage by the maximum supply current, which is 20 volts multiplied by 0.1 amp, or 2 watts, in the example given above.

An important point to bear in mind if this method has to be used is that the supply voltage fed to the circuit under test will be less than normal, since the supply voltage has effectively been reduced to the point where an excessive supply current no longer flows. This will obviously have a substantial effect on most, if not all the voltages in the circuit, and interpreting results is consequently made somewhat more difficult than would otherwise be the case.

A power amplifier circuit such as the one shown in Figure 5 is the type of equipment that is most likely to give problems with an excessive current consumption. A fault in the output stage, which handles very high currents under peak signal conditions, is likely to cause a very large current flow. Apart from the more obvious things like short circuits across one of the output transistors, it should be remembered that a fault in the driver stage could also produce a large current flow through the output transistors.

The purpose of D1 and D2 is to give a forward bias to Tr3 and Tr4 so that they pass a small bias current under quiescent conditions and cross over distortion is avoided. In practice these diodes might actually be replaced with a transistor used in the amplified diode configuration, or perhaps a variable resistance might be used in addition to the diodes to permit the desired quiescent output current to be set. If this bias circuit provides even a marginally high voltage a very high quiescent current will flow through the output devices.

Even if the supply voltage is only around 2 volts, voltage tests might give some valuable clues about the nature of the fault. For example, it might be found that there is no voltage, or very little voltage across R3, possibly indicating that this component is very low in value or has gone closed circuit. If the supply voltage is several volts, the voltage at the emitter of Tr3 is about 0.65 volts or so lower, and there is very little voltage across R3, this would tend to suggest that Tr3 and R3 are operating properly and that the lower section of the circuit is faulty. One possibility is a break in the current path through D1 and D2. Tr3 and R3 would then act as a straight forward emitter follower stage having Tr4 as its emitter load. The output voltage would be approximately correct since it would need to rise to its normal operating level in order to bias Tr1 and Tr2 into conduction so that these could bias Tr4 into conduction. No significant current could flow through the output transistors until this output voltage had been achieved, but only a marginally higher voltage causes a massive output current to flow as Tr3 and Tr4 are both then biased hard into conduction. The current limiting therefore results in the supply voltage stabilising at a little over half its normal operating level.

The problem could be due to a mechanical fault, or perhaps a fault in D1 or D2. A point that should be borne in mind when using diodes is that although the band around one end of the component's body normally indicates the cathode (+) end, I have come across diodes where the band is at the opposite end, and have heard of others who have also found this. It might therefore be worthwhile checking that the polarity of the diodes is indicated correctly. Component testing will be covered later on.

Isolation

When testing a large circuit that is difficult to test due to an excessive current consumption, a useful technique is to try cutting the supply to various parts of the circuit. The idea of this is simply that when the supply to the offending stage is cut the overload on the supply will be removed and the search for the fault will have been considerably narrowed down.

This technique can be useful when testing logic circuits since voltage tests are likely to be completely meaningless with a very low supply voltage, logic testers will probably fail to work at all, and faultless parts of the circuit will probably fail to operate as well. Cutting the supply to various stages of the

circuit is usually quite simple as it merely entails unplugging
integrated circuits from the circuit board. However, it is not
advisable to unplug or fit integrated circuits into their holders
while power is applied to a circuit as this could possible result in
damage to the integrated circuits.

The same basic technique may also be usable with linear
circuits that use a number of integrated circuits. It is not a
technique that could be easily applied to a circuit of the type
shown in Figure 5 where only two stages are present, and where
cutting the supply to the driver stage could be expected to
remove the overload even if the fault was in the output stage.

Incorrect Voltages

Since it is unlikely that you will always be very familiar with
the circuitry and components employed in the projects that
you construct it is inevitable that sooner or later you will be
faced with test voltage readings that do not agree with those
given on a circuit diagram or test chart, but will not really be
able to glean from the test results the precise nature of the
fault. It can sometimes happen that test results do not give a
clear indication as to the precise fault even if you are familiar
with the circuitry and components used in the project.

Under these conditions it is necessary to check for mechanical
faults as thoroughly as possible, and to check components in
the viscinity of the incorrect test voltages. Fault finding almost
invariably ends in this way anyway, but hopefully in most
cases the area of the fault will be reduced to just one or two
possibilities so that minimal further testing will then be required

Estimating Voltages

As mentioned at the beginning of this chapter, even if a circuit
diagram does not give test voltages and no test voltage chart is
provided either, it is often possible to estimate voltages at various
points in a circuit and thus find any points in the circuit where
a substantial error is present. A certain amount of technical
knowledge is needed in order to do this, but it is well
worthwhile acquiring this knowledge as it can often greatly
simplify what would otherwise be a fairly difficult and long

fault-finding job.

The earlier discussion of the circuit shown in Figure 5 should give some insight into how this voltage estimation can be achieved, and the circuit diagram of Figure 6 plus the following notes should help to further clarify this point. This is the circuit of a speech processor featured in the book "C.B. Projects" by the same publisher and author as this publication, and full details of this project can be found in the above mentioned book. This project has been chosen simply because it illustrates a number of useful points.

The basic action of the circuit is to amplify a weak microphone signal using a two stage amplifier (Tr1 and Tr2) to produce a high enough signal level to give soft clipping by D1, D2 and R6. Tr3 and D3 are used to give a visual indication of the degree of clipping used, and Tr4 is used as the basis of a low pass filter which reduces high frequency distortion products on the output signal. The purpose of the unit is to increase the average signal level without increasing the peak signal level. This gives a signal of apparent greater volume but does not cause overloading of the CB transmitter.

If we start with the input amplifier; this is a simple common emitter amplifier based on Tr1. R1 is the bias resistor, and it is normal for any amplifier to be biased so that its output voltage is approximately equal to half the supply voltage so that the highest possible overload margin is obtained. It is therefore reasonable to assume that the voltage at the collector of Tr1 is something in the region of 4.5 volts, although with the simple method of biasing used in this circuit an error of about 2 volts either side of this would not be surprising.

The current in emitter resistor R3 will be only marginally different to that in the collector resistor, R2, since the collector and emitter currents of any reasonably high gain transistor used in a linear circuit are virtually identical. There is about half the supply voltage across R2, and with 4.5 volts across 4k7 this obviously gives a collector current and (hence emitter current) of just under 1mA (4.5 volts divided by 4k7 = 0.957mA). It is not really necessary to do any precise mathematics here, and an estimated current of just under 1mA is quite good enough.

A current of 1mA through a 330 ohm resistor gives a voltage of 0.33 volts, and a voltage slightly below this figure

27

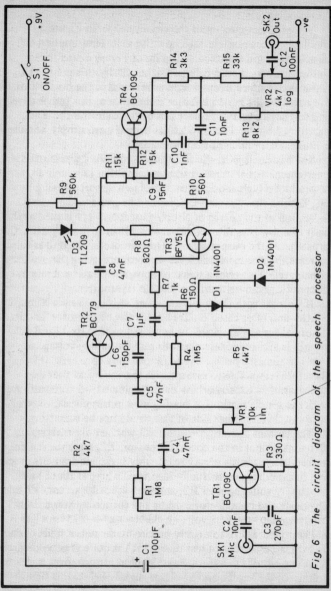

Fig. 6 The circuit diagram of the speech processor

28

would therefore be expected at the emitter of Tr1. It is not really necessary to work this out using Ohm's Law, and it is merely necessary to remember that with a current of 1mA one volt is developed for each kilohm of resistance, which is obviously 0.33 volts for a resistance of 330 ohms (0.33k). This system can be used with other currents, and a flow of 100μA gives one volt per 10 kilohms of resistance, and 10mA develops one volt for every one hundred ohms of resistance. This method can be readily extended to suit any current, and is often a convenient aid to estimating circuit voltages. Remember that the point of the exercise is to give a rough estimation of voltages in the circuit so that any obvious errors can be detected, and that it is probably a waste of time to resort to involved calculations.

If we return to the input stage of the speech processor, if the voltage across R2 is more than 4.5 volts (or the collector voltage of Tr1 is less than 4.5 volts in other words) the voltage across R3 will be similarly higher than expected. In the same way, reduced voltage across R2 (higher voltage at Tr1's collector) should give a correspondingly lower voltage across R3. This is simply because an error in the voltage across R2 will mean that the collector and emitter currents of Tr1 are other than the expected figure of just under 1mA, and the voltages developed across both resistors will change proportionately.

As stated earlier, in practice it is quite likely that due to component tolerances the output voltage from Tr1 will be perhaps a volt or two above or below the half supply voltage point. If there is a fault in this stage it is likely that the collector voltage will be at virtually the full positive supply potential, or that the collector and emitter terminals of Tr1 will both be at about the same voltage (about 0.6 volts or so).

A very high collector voltage would suggest that Tr1 is faulty or not connected into circuit properly, or that R1 is not providing a base bias current to Tr1 for some reason. With little or no voltage across the collector and emitter of Tr1, it is likely that Tr1 has gone closed circuit, there is a short circuit between collector and emitter of Tr1 or R1 has gone very low in value and is giving an excessive base current (or it is short circuited).

The voltage at the base of Tr1 should be about 0.65 volts plus the emitter potential of about 0.3 volts, or just under one volt in other words. However, the base voltage is obtained via the very high 1M8 resistance of R1, and the current flowing in this part of the circuit is only about $2\mu A$. An ordinary multimeter would give a voltage reading of little more than zero if used to measure this point in the circuit, and any significant voltage reading here would suggest a fault. An electronic multimeter would give a reasonably accurate voltage reading, although it would still probably give a reading somewhat below the expected figure.

The voltage reading across the input socket should be zero, except perhaps for a very small initial indication from the meter as C2 charges up. The purpose of C2 is to prevent a current flowing from the base of Tr1 to the microphone (which would upset the biasing of Tr1 and prevent the unit from operating, and could harm the microphone). Any significant voltage reading across the input socket would be indicative of a mechanical fault of some kind or C2 itself being faulty with a high leakage level.

C4 couples the output signal of Tr1 to volume control VR1, and prevents a direct current flowing. C5 couples the output signal at the wiper connection of VR1 to the next stage of the circuit and again provides DC blocking. There should be 0V at both the top track connection of VR1 and at the wiper terminal of this component.

Tr2 is used in a common emitter amplifier that is similar to the stage using Tr1, but the fact that a PNP device is utilized rather than an NPN transistor means that the transistor and load resistor (R5) are swopped over in order to give voltages of the correct polarity to the transistor. Another difference is that Tr2 has no external emitter resistor.

About half the supply voltage would therefore be expected at the collector of Tr2, and the base terminal should be about 0.65 volts below the positive supply rail voltage. This last voltage is at a high impedance in a sense, but the current to drive the meter is not obtained through the bias resistor in this case, but is obtained by way of the base-emitter junction of Tr2. This can provide plenty of current and an accurate reading should be obtained (although the biasing of Tr2 will be upset while the meter is in circuit due to the increased base current).

C3 and C6 are used to reduce the high frequency bandwidth of the circuit, and these do not have any effect on the DC conditions of the circuit (unless one of them is faulty, of course).

C7 couples the output of the second amplifier stage to the clipping circuit, but it blocks any direct current flow. This gives zero volts at the junction of C7, C8, R6 and R7, and also at the junction of R6, D1 and D2. This prevents any input bias current being fed to Tr3 under quiescent conditions, giving zero volts at the base of Tr3 as well.

As Tr3 is cut off under quiescent conditions its collector is at almost the full positive supply rail potential. However, even if this voltage is measured with an electronic multimeter it is likely that there will be a voltage drop of about 1.5 to 2 volts through D3 (due to its low value there will be no significant voltage drop through R8). Although one might expect a voltage drop of only about 0.6 volts or so through D3, LEDs are not silicon diodes and have a much higher forward conduction threshold voltage. It should also be borne in mind that germanium diodes have a much lower forward threshold voltage than silicon types, and usually give a voltage drop of only about 0.1 volts or so. The base emitter threshold voltage of a germanium transistor is similarly low, although germanium transistors are only rarely found in new project designs.

Of course, the voltage at the junction of R8 and D3 should also be about 1.5 to 2 volts below the positive supply potential. If zero volts or only a very low voltage reading was to be obtained at these last two test points it would suggest that D3 was either faulty or connected with the wrong polarity. The latter is probably the more likely explanation since there are a number of leadout identification methods in use. Many LEDs have one leadout wire shorter than the other, and it is usually the cathode leadout that is the shorter of the two. There are a few LEDs that have the anode as the shorter of the two though, and this could easily lead to confusion and connection errors!

With an input applied to the unit and VR1 well advanced, D3 should light up and the collector voltage of Tr3 should reduce somewhat. A simple test such as this can be very helpful as the location of the fault can be immediately narrowed down

31

slightly. If this test gives the correct result it is almost certain that the fault is in the circuitry to the right of Tr3, since the circuitry to the left of Tr3 seems to be functioning correctly. If the test does not give the desired result, then the fault is almost certainly in the circuitry around or to the left of Tr3.

Unfortunately most circuits do not conveniently have a signal indicator about half way through the circuit, or anything comparable to this, and fault finding in this way is probably not then possible. With a little ingenuity it is often possible to deduce some useful information before making any proper test and measurements on the faulty equipment. For example, if a transistor radio becomes faulty with only low volume and distorted output, but with good sensitivity on all wavebands, this would suggest that the RF, mixer and IF stages of the set are functioning normally, and that the fault lies in either the detector or audio stages of the set. On the other hand, if the set was found to be functioning properly on all but one waveband it is virtually certain that the fault lies in the RF or mixer circuitry which is only associated with the faulty waveband, and it would hardly be worthwhile making detailed checks on the IF detector and audio stages.

If we now return to the circuit of Figure 6, the final stage of the circuit is an active filter based on Tr4. The latter is used in the emitter follower mode with biasing provided R9 and R10, but the bias is applied to Tr4 via R11 and R12 (which are part of the filter circuitry and couple the bias to Tr4 only as a secondary function).

The values of R9 and R10 are identical, and they would therefore be expected to give about half the supply potential at the junction of the two components. However, the series resistance of the input impedance of Tr4 plus R11 and R12 shunts R10 slightly, and the actual voltage at the junction of R9 and R10 would probably be a little under 4 volts. The voltage at the junction of R11 and R12 would be just marginally less than this due to the voltage drop across R11, and the voltage at the base of Tr4 would be marginally lower still due to the additional voltage drop through R12.

It is important to bear in mind though that R9 and R10 have a quite high value, and the current flowing in this part of the circuit is only a few microamps. Unless voltage checks are made using an electronic multimeter the voltage readings obtained should be very low, with probably well under 1 volt being indicated in each case.

The voltage reading obtained varies significantly according to the measuring range used when an ordinary multimeter is used to measure a voltage in a high impedance circuit. This is simply because the resistance through the multimeter increases in proportion to the full scale voltage reading. For instance, a 20k per volt multimeter set to its 5 volt FSD (full scale deflection) range will have a resistance of 100k (20k x 5 = 100k). When switched to the 25 volts range the resistance becomes 500k (20k x 25 = 500k). Even a 500k resistance would probably reduce voltage readings by about half when checking the potentials around the base circuit of Tr4, but this compares with a reduction of about 80% or so when using the 5 volt range with its 100k resistance.

This increase in the voltage reading as the multimeter is switched to a higher voltage range can be used to check that a low voltage reading is produced by the loading of the multimeter rather than a fault producing a genuinely low voltage. Unfortunately it is not possible to use an ordinary multimeter on a high voltage range in order to obtain a resistance comparable to that of an electronic multimeter when making tests on low voltage circuitry. This is due to the fact that the accuracy of a multimeter is normally expressed as a percentage (typically about 2%) of the full scale value. On (say) the 10 volt range of a multimeter this would give an accuracy of plus or minus 0.2 volts, and a potential of a couple of volts or so could obviously be measured with reasonable accuracy. On the 100 volt range, and again assuming a 2% of full scale accuracy, the reading obtained would have a guaranteed accuracy of only plus or minus 2 volts. This would obviously give hoplessly unreliable results when measuring a potential of only about 2 volts or so.

The voltage at the emitter of Tr4 should be about 0.6 volts or thereabouts below the base potential, or at about 3.3 volts in other words. This voltage is at a low impedance and using an ordinary multimeter should give accurate results. If this reading is correct, then it is quite likely that the base bias circuitry is satisfactory. R14, R15 and VR2 form a three element potential divider, and without resorting to any complex calculations it can be seen that R14 represents something less than 10% of the total resistance in this divider circuit. Thus the voltage at the junction of R14 and R15 should be just slightly less than that at the emitter of Tr4, or around 3 volts in other words. VR2 represents something over 10% of the total resistance through the potential divider circuit, and the voltage at the junction of R15 and VR2 should thus be something in the region of 0.4 volts (i.e. a little over 10% of the voltage at the emitter of Tr4). The voltage at the slider terminal of VR2 should vary from zero at the bottom (negative supply) end of its track to about 0.4 volts when it is at the top (R15) end of its track.

If the voltage at the junction of R15 and VR2 was to be found to vary when VR2 was adjusted, this would suggest that this control was faulty or incorrectly connected. Similarly, zero volts or any constant potential at the wiper terminal of VR2 would suggest a faulty component or incorrect connection. Short circuits can occur quite easily when wiring up potentiometers, as well as many other types of controls, sockets, etc. for that matter. This is most likely to occur with the modern miniature potentiometers, sockets, etc., which are now becoming increasingly popular, especially if you are a little over-generous with the solder, or strip an excessive amount of sleeving from wires that connect to controls and sockets so that there are lengths of bare wire that can short together.

The voltage across the output socket should be zero due to the DC blocking provided by C12, although the pointer of the meter might give a slight jump when the meter is initially connected and C12 charges up. Sockets are often a source of problems, particularly jack sockets having unused make or break contacts, since it is then very easy to accidentally make connections to the wrong tags. If there is any doubt about the correct way of wiring up a socket it is a good idea to fit a plug into the socket so that a continuity tester can be used to check exactly what tag of the socket connects to what tag of the plug. Make and break contacts can also be checked using a continuity tester while inserting and removing the plug from the socket.

Finally, the voltage check that should always be made first is a check of the supply voltage. In the case of battery operated equipment this is not just a matter of measuring the battery voltage, but measuring the voltage actually fed to the circuit. Leads can easily break away inside battery clips, and switches are basically mechanical components that are more likely to be faulty than purely electronic components such as transistors and diodes. Failure of the supply to get through to the main circuit is not an uncommon cause of a newly built project failing to work.

Although a battery may have a nominal voltage of (say) 9 volts, bear in mind that the actual voltage of a battery may differ quite significantly from this figure without the battery being unusable. A fresh 9 volt battery usually has an actual voltage of about 9.5 volts off load, and the internal resistance of a fresh battery is comparatively low and under load there is not likely to be a substantial reduction in this figure.

As a battery ages its voltage tends to reduce substantially, and its internal resistance rises. This gives a loaded voltage that is often well below the nominal battery potential, and a 9 volt battery can have a loaded voltage of down to about 7.5 volts before needing replacement.

The above is true of ordinary layer and zinc-carbon cells, but is not true of most other types of cell such as lithium, mercury, and NiCad types. These tend to have a much more stable output potential and internal resistance.

Mains Powered Projects

When making voltage checks on mains powered equipment it is obviously necessary to take great care to avoid dangerous electric shocks from the mains supply. Electronic workshops should really have power sockets fed from the mains via an isolation transformer (i.e. a double wound mains transformer having 240 volt primary and secondary windings), but few amateur workshops are equipped in this way.

Most mains powered electronic projects incorporate a mains isolation transformer which has a low voltage output, and one of the supply rail of the equipment is usually earthed. This gives little danger of a severe electric shock from most of the circuit provided a serious mistake in the construction of the unit has not been made. It is essential to thoroughly check the power supply of a mains powered project before switching the unit on, and the temptation to just give a cursory check here should be overcome. Remember that it is not just the project that could be harmed if there is a mistake in this wiring! A typical mains power supply circuit is shown in Figure 7.

When making checks on mains powered equipment be very careful not to come into contact with any part of the circuit that is at the mains potential, and ideally all exposed mains wiring should be insulated at the construction stage. It will of course be necessary to remove this insulation if any testing of this wiring becomes necessary at a later date, and be sure to unplug the unit from the mains before removing the insulation.

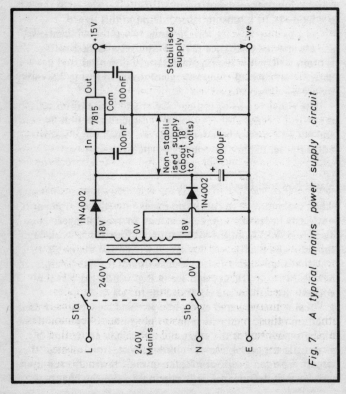

Fig. 7 A typical mains power supply circuit

Simply switching off at the mains outlet or at the on/off switch of the equipment is not sufficient, and would probably result in a severe electric shock being sustained.

Most testing of the mains wiring can actually be carried out with the unit unplugged from the mains since it is largely or even totally a matter of checking that there is continuity from the mains plug to the other end of the mains lead, checking that fuses have not blown, testing on/off switches, and other tests that can be made with a continuity tester. It obviously makes sense to make tests that are completely safe where this is possible rather than to make checks with the mains supply present.

If it is necessary to measure points in the circuit which are at the mains supply potential, apart from taking care to avoid touching any of the mains wiring, be careful to avoid bridging points in the circuit with the test prods as this could be dangerous and would almost certainly cause expensive damage. There is little risk using the type of prod that has a small metal clip at the end, but greater care has to be exercised when using the type that have long metal prods.

If a fuse blows when the unit is switched on, and when replaced the new fuse also blows at switch-on, there is no point in continually replacing the fuse. There is a fault which is causing the fuse to blow and prevent serious damage to the unit, and the fault must be located and rectified before the fuse is replaced and the unit is switched on again.

If the fuse is in the mains wiring it is likely that the cause of the problem is a faulty switch, faulty transformer, or something of this nature which can be traced using a continuity tester. It is possible for a fault on the secondary side of the mains transformer to cause a fuse in the primary circuit of the transformer to blow, but this is unlikely to occur due to the rather generous ratings of the fuses that are normally used in the primary circuits of power supplies.

When constructing projects bear in mind that mains fuses other than those mounted in mains plugs should be mounted in panel mounting fuseholders and not chassis mounting or printed circuit types. Panel mounting types are designed so that the fuse can be changed safely even if the mains supply is inadvertently left connected to the unit while the change is

37

made. With chassis and printed circuit fuseholders this is not the case, and changing the fuse with the mains supply connected would almost certainly result in a severe electric shock being received.

If a fuse in the secondary circuit of the mains transformer blows it is likely that the fault lies in the supply circuitry rather than in the main circuitry, but it will probably be possible to verify this by breaking one of the supply leads to the main circuit so that the supply can be tested independently. A fuse blowing in the secondary circuit of a mains transformer cannot be caused by a fault which only affects the primary circuit of the transformer.

The voltage produced across the smoothing capacitor of the power supply is likely to be much higher off-load than when the supply is fully loaded, and could be as much as 50% higher. Also, the fact that a mains transformer has a voltage rating of (say) 15 volts does not mean that 15 volts will be produced across the smoothing capacitor. The 15 volt rating is likely to be a loaded RMS figure and the capacitor will charge to the peak voltage (less a small voltage drop through the rectifier circuit) not the RMS one. Thus the unloaded voltage across the smoothing capacitor could be more than 50% higher than the transformer's voltage rating.

If a stabilised supply is used then the output should be within a few percent of the stated output voltage under full or zero loading. Even under full load the input voltage to the stabiliser circuit would normally be a couple of volts or so more than the output voltage since there is always a voltage loss through a series stabiliser.

There are a number of faults that can easily occur in the secondary side of a mains power supply, such as a rectifier or transformer connected incorrectly, or a capacitor that has a very high leakage level. As most modern power supply circuits, including stabilised ones, are very simple, it is unlikely that any real difficulty will be experienced when trying to track down the fault.

There are a few home-constructor projects that are mains operated and do not include an isolation and step-down transformer. Mains power controllers are an example of a project of this type. Fault-finding on equipment of this type while it is connected to the mains supply is rather hazardous and is not to be recommended. It is better to thoroughly check the circuit for mechanical faults and errors, and try component testing if this fails to bring results.

With the more complex circuits of this type it may be necessary to resort to voltage tests, and it is strongly recommended that the equipment should then be supplied via an isolation transformer (commercial workshops and test laboratories are required by law to have a supply obtained via such a transformer). Even with such a transformer in use there are still high voltages present in the circuit which could give a dangerous electric shock.

The usual procedure when dealing with equipment of this type is to clip the appropriate test prod to the point in the circuit to which test voltages are related while the unit is disconnected from the supply. Check that the unit is disconnected before doing this. After connecting the supply, one hand is used to manipulate the other test prod while the other hand is kept in a pocket. The idea of doing this is simply that it is not possible to have you hands across a high voltage source in the circuit while one hand is safely in a pocket and well away from the circuitry. It would still be possible to get an electric shock through the hand which is used to direct the test prod, but this would probably give no more than a violent jolt (which would be well worth avoiding) and would not be as serious as a shock from one hand to the other with a current flowing across the body.

Signal Injector/Tracer

An alternative to voltage checks is to feed an input signal into the equipment and then check the signal obtained at various points in the circuit, or to inject a signal at various points in the circuit in an attempt to obtain a correct output signal. This system is obviously not applicable to every type of electronic equipment, but can be employed with virtually any piece of audio or radio equipment, as well as certain types of test gear such as AC millivoltmeters and some other types of equipment. It is a method which is likely to be of little use with items of equipment such as power supplies and model train controllers.

In order to use this system it is necessary to have equipment that can be used to provide a suitable input signal (a signal injector) and detect the signal present at various points in the circuit (a signal tracer). While the signal could be provided by several complex signal generators covering a wide frequency range and having various output waveforms, etc., advanced test equipment is by no means essential for simple testing of this type. The most popular type of signal injector is actually just a simple oscillator operating at a middle audio frequency but having an output waveform that gives strong harmonics (multiples of the fundamental frequency) up to frequencies of several Megahertz or more. The fundamental and low frequency harmonics give a signal suitable for audio testing, and the high frequency harmonics give an RF test signal.

Likewise, a signal tracer can consist of a complex set-up including a sensitive amplifier, oscilloscope, RF probes and an AC millivoltmeter. However, a high gain amplifier feeding a crystal earphone is often just as effective for this purpose.

The circuit diagram of a very simple signal injector and tracer is shown in Figure 8. IC1 is used in the signal tracer and IC2 is the basis of the signal injector.

IC1 is used as what is really just a straight forward inverting mode operational amplifier circuit with the non-inverting input biased by R2 and R3. C3 filters out any stray feedback which might otherwise cause instability. R1 and R4 are a negative feedback network and these set the voltage gain of the amplifier at around 45 times with an input impedance of about 220k. A gain of about 45 times is quite sufficient since the output of the unit is fed to a crystal earphone, and these are quite capable of producing an output of reasonable volume from an input of just a few tens of millivolts. This circuit will therefore give an audible output from an input signal of well under a millivolt. The output of IC1 is coupled direct to the earphone and no DC blocking capacitor is required here.

VR1 is a sensitivity control, and is a simple volume control type variable attenuator. C2 provides DC blocking between VR1 and the input of the amplifier while C1 provides DC blocking at the input of the unit. It is important to have a capacitor at the input of the circuit as the resistance of VR1 could otherwise cause a malfunction in the circuit under test

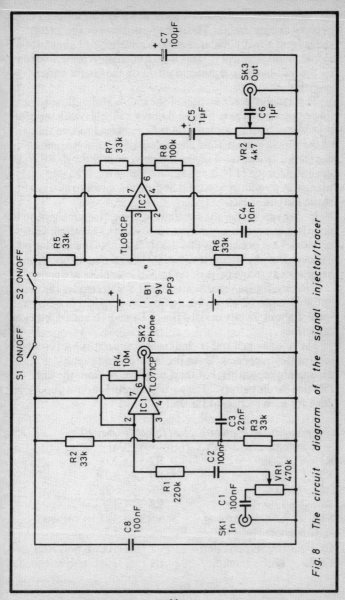

Fig.8 The circuit diagram of the signal injector/tracer

41

if it was to be connected to a point in the circuit having a high impedance bias circuit. The input impedance of the circuit varies from about 470k at minimum sensitivity to about 150k at maximum sensitivity. This is high enough to prevent loading by the unit having a significant effect on the circuit under investigation.

The signal injector section of the unit is also built around a single operational amplifier, and this is a simple oscillator of the type where timing capacitor C4 is first charged to two thirds of the supply voltage from the output of IC2 via R8, and then discharged to one third of the supply voltage through R8 and the output stage of IC2, and so on. This gives a roughly triangular waveform across C4 and a good quality squarewave at the output of IC2.

In this application the squarewave is the obvious signal to use since it is at a much lower impedance and the required RF harmonics are present on this signal. The fundamental output frequency of the circuit is about 1kHz, and reasonably strong harmonics at frequencies of up to 5MHz or more are present.

VR2 is a simple variable attenuator which enables the output level to be set anywhere from zero up to a maximum level of about 7 volts peak to peak. C5 and C6 are DC blocking capacitors.

The injector and tracer circuits have separate on/off switches (S1 for the tracer and S2 for the injector) and supply decoupling capacitors, but they are powered from the same PP3 size 9 volt battery. The current consumption is about 2mA for each section of the unit.

Components for Signal Injector/Tracer (Figure 8)
   Resistors, all 1/3 watt 5% (10% over 1M)

R1	220k	R2	33k
R3	33k	R4	10M
R5	33k	R6	33k
R7	33k	R8	100k
VR1	470k log carbon	VR2	4k7 lin carbon

   Capacitors

C1	100nF polyester	C2	100nF polyester
C3	22nF ceramic	C4	10nF polyester

C5	1μF 63V electrolytic	C6	1μF polyester or
C7	100μF 10V		carbonate
	electrolytic	C8	100nF polyester

Semiconductors

| IC1 | TL071CP | IC2 | TL081CP |

Switches

| S1 | Miniature SPST toggle | S2 | Miniature SPST toggle |

Miscellaneous

0.1in matrix stripboard
Metal case
PP3 size battery and connector to suit
Two control knobs
Three 3.5mm jack sockets (SK1–SK3)
Test leads, wire, solder, etc.

Construction

Most of the components are assembled on a 0.1in matrix
stripboard having 12 copper strips by 29 holes, and the
component layout and other details of the board and wiring
are shown in Figure 9.

C1 and C6 are not mounted on the component panel, but
are instead mounted direct between the appropriate
potentiometers and sockets. In other respects construction of
the unit is very straight forward. Although both IC1 and IC2
have FET input stages, these are JFET and not MOSFET
devices and do not need any special handling precautions.

In Use

If we first consider the use of the unit as a signal injector, let
us first assume that the unit is to be used to check a simple
circuit of the type discussed earlier, and shown in the circuit
diagram of Figure 5. With this type of testing it is normal to
start at the output and gradually work back through the
circuit towards the input. At some stage the signal will fail to
appear at the output of the circuit under test, and the fault
then probably lies in the circuitry immediately after the point
where the last test was made (although it might be in the
circuitry at the point where the last test was made).

In the same way that testing a circuit of the type shown in
Figure 5 can be difficult using voltage tests, it can also be

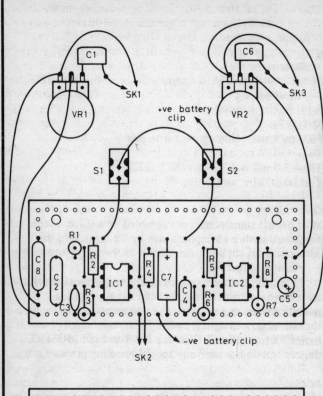

Fig. 9 Constructional details of the signal injector/tracer

44

difficult to make meaningful tests using a signal injector or tracer. The problem is that the direct coupling makes the circuit effectively a single stage, and it would not be easy to separate one part of the circuit from another so that each part could be individually tested. However, it is still possible to make some useful tests using a signal injector, and even if this does not show up the precise fault, it should at least eliminate a few possibilities. This is an important point since fault finding is often a matter of ascertaining which parts of a circuit function properly until the only remaining stage must by a process of elimination be the faulty one (although hopefully in most cases the fault will be found before this final stage is reached).

The first two tests using the signal injector would be to test LS1 and C2. Remember that a failure to obtain a proper output from the unit does not necessarily mean that the circuit is faulty! It could simply be that the loudspeaker is faulty, or that the output is failing to reach the loudspeaker due to a break or short circuit in the loudspeaker lead.

In order to test the loudspeaker the output of the tracer could simply be connected directly across the loudspeaker, and with the output level control of the signal injector set at maximum this might give a quiet audio tone from the loud-speaker. Do not expect a loud tone as the output power of the signal injector is not very great, and even a sensitive high impedance loudspeaker will not give very much volume.

If no tone, or a barely audible tone is obtained this does not necessarily mean that the loudspeaker is faulty. The output impedance of an audio power amplifier is very low, and this impedance is effectively shunted across the loudspeaker. This could reduce the power received by the loudspeaker to such a low level that no significant audio output would be produced. A simple way around this is to temporarily disconnect the positive terminal of output coupling capacitor C2 so that this shunting effect is removed. By coupling the output of the signal injector to the loudspeaker via C2 it is then possible to test this component. Coupling the output of the signal injector to the negative terminal of C2 (assuming no signal from the previous test reached the loudspeaker) would determine whether the fault was due to C2 going open circuit or a a break in the loudspeaker lead. If all tests give negative results it is likely that the loudspeaker is faulty, and completely disconnecting it from the circuit and then applying the output of the signal injector to this component should verify this. The fault could be a short circuit in the loudspeaker lead, and a continuity tester could be used to test for this. However, disconnect the lead from LS1 before making this test as LS1, even if operational, will place a very low resistance across the speaker lead.

The fault could be due to C2 being connected with the wrong polarity, or having a very low leakage resistance. Under these circumstances tests with the signal injector could be misleading since C2 would couple the output of the unit to the loudspeaker quite well. This is a fault which should be easily spotted though, since there will be high quiescent loading on the power supply, C2 is likely to get quite warm to the touch or even quite hot, and a voltage check across LS1 would reveal a strong DC potential instead of zero volts.

The input coupling capacitor (C1) could be tested by applying the signal from the signal injector direct to the base of Tr1, and if this gives an output signal it is likely that C1 is faulty, or possible there is a mechanical fault such as a broken PCB track or a dry joint here.

It is probably not worthwhile making tests with the output of the signal injector coupled to the bases of Tr3 and Tr4 as it would be difficult to put any meaningful interpretation on the results obtained.

Using the Tracer

While faults can be found quite rapidly and easily with the aid of a signal injector, I prefer to use a signal tracer (although not everyone has this preference by any means). The basic method of fault finding using a signal tracer is to first apply an input signal to the circuit under test, and then try to detect this signal at various points in the circuit using the signal tracer, starting at the input and working towards the output.

If we consider the use of a signal tracer on the Speech Processor circuit of Figure 6, the first task is obviously to provide a suitable input signal for the unit. This could be provided by the signal injector, but there are two slight problems if this method is adopted. Firstly there is inevitably a small amount of breakthrough from the injector to the tracer, and this could cause a certain amount of confusion when using the two circuits simultaneously, although the amount of breakthrough will probably not be sufficient for this to be a major problem. Secondly, and of greater importance, the type of output signal produced by the signal tracer is such that it could tend to mask a fault. Where this is most likely to happen is where the fault is causing a badly distorted output with possibly an attendant small loss of gain, rather than producing little or no output signal at all. On signals such as speech, music, or a reasonably pure sinewave, the new frequencies produced by severe distortion are very obvious, but this is not the case with a squarewave. A clipped squarewave remains a squarewave, with a small loss of amplitude being the only real consequence of the clipping!

It would therefore be better, especially if the fault is of a type that causes severe distortion, to use some other type of input signal. This could be a sinewave from a signal generator, with the output level set to give an output comparable to that of a high impedance microphone (say about 2 millivolts or so). The output from the earphone socket of a radio or cassette recorder could be used, although it would be necessary to include a high value resistor in series with the output in order to reduce it to a level comparable to that of a microphone. Another alternative would be to use a microphone, with a suitable sound signal being obtained by, for example, placing the microphone on a radio set having the volume turned well back so as not to overdrive the microphone and the processor.

As pointed out earlier, the Speech Processor circuit has what is effectively a simple signal tracer about half way through the circuit in the form of LED indicator D3 and its associated circuitry. With VR1 well advanced D3 should light up during signal peaks, and if it fails to do so this suggests that the signal is not reaching this part of the circuit and that the fault is therefore in the earlier circuitry around Tr1 and Tr2. Obviously most circuits will not have a signal indicator conveniently situated somewhere in the middle of the circuit, and it may then be worthwhile making the first test at some point roughly half way through the circuit. The point of doing this is that it immediately enables one half of the circuit to be assumed to be functioning correctly, and prevents time being wasted making lengthy checks on this part of the unit. If you obtain a proper signal half way through the circuit then it is reasonable to assume that the circuitry ahead of and around the point at which the test was made is not faulty. Subsequent checks are then made at various points further into the circuit, gradually working from the mid-way point towards the output. When a proper signal is not obtained the fault lies in the circuitry in the immediate vicinity of the last test point.

If a proper signal is not obtained at the test point half way through the circuit it is likely that the fault lies somewhere earlier in the circuit, or possibly in the circuitry around the point where the test was made. The possibility of a fault in the circuitry later in the unit cannot be ruled out at this stage, but the first job is to locate the fault or faults in the first half of the circuit. If the unit then still fails to operate properly checks can be made in the second half of the unit.

Let us assume that D3 does not light up, and that a check with the signal tracer does not reveal any significant signal present at the junction of R6, R7, etc. (the test with the signal tracer is necessary to ensure that the D3 is not failing to light due to a fault in the LED driver circuit rather than due to the lack of a suitable driver signal). Subsequent tests can either be made working forwards from the last test point towards the input of the circuit, or from the input of the circuit working towards the centre of the circuit. I prefer the second method, and this is the one we will pursue here.

The first test would be made to the left hand side of C2 to ensure that the signal is reaching the circuit board, and that the problem is not due to a short circuited socket or something of this nature. The next check would be made to the other side of C2 (i.e. the base of Tr1) to check that the signal is being properly coupled through C2. It should be borne in mind that a lack of signal at the input of the circuit does not necessarily mean that the signal is not reaching C2, or that C2 is failing to couple the signal to the base of Tr1. It could be that a short circuit from one end of the circuit to the negative supply rail (or possibly some other part of the circuit) is causing the problem. As always, care must be taken when interpreting results, and component tests and checks with a continuity tester may well be necessary before the exact nature of the fault can be determined. The signal at the input of the unit will be at a very low level and the signal tracer will probably need to be at virtually maximum sensitivity in order to obtain an output at good volume.

The situation is different at the collector of Tr1, and the signal here is well over 20dB (10 times) stronger. In order to obtain a comparable volume it should therefore be necessary to substantially back off the sensitivity control. The signal at the emitter of Tr1 should be virtually the same as that at the base. In some common emitter amplifiers there is an emitter resistor (like R3 in this circuit), but it is bypassed by a fairly high value capacitor. This is done so that the emitter resistor introduces negative feedback that is used to help give a stable and predictable bias to the stage, but the capacitor eliminates AC negative feedback so that the gain of the stage is not reduced. A typical common emitter amplifier of this type is shown in the circuit diagram of Figure 10. Obviously there should be

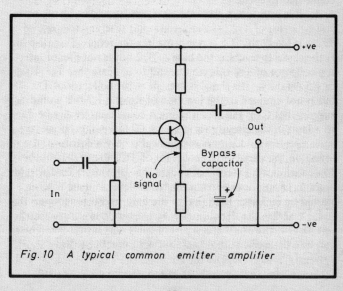

Fig. 10 A typical common emitter amplifier

no audio signal present at the emitter of the transistor used in this type of circuit, and if a signal is detected here it would suggest that the bypass capacitor is not working properly (which would give a very large reduction in the amplification provided by the circuit).

Assuming that a suitable signal is detected at the collector of Tr1, and the input stage of the circuit is functioning correctly, the next test would be made at the non-earthy end of VR1's track to ensure that C4 is coupling the signal to VR1 properly. The next test would be at the wiper terminal of VR1, and VR1 should be adjusted over its full range of settings to ensure that the signal can be varied from zero to its full level in the correct manner.

Faults can occur in potentiometers of course, but these are normally fairly obvious. A well used potentiometer may become noisy when adjusted, and a broken track can result in the signal being at either full or minimum level depending on which side of the crack the wiper is set. If a potentiometer used in a volume control type circuit seems to have little effect this usually just indicates that the lower end of the track is not connected to earth.

If all is well so far, then the next tests would be at the base and collector of Tr2. If the signal is not reaching the base of Tr2 it is likely that C5 is not providing the required signal path. If the signal is reaching the base of Tr2 but is not present at the collector of Tr2 this would tend to indicate that Tr2, R4 or R5 is faulty. If a signal is present at the collector of Tr2 but is not coupled to the junction of R6 and R7 this would suggest that C7 is faulty, although it could conceivably be due to a fault in the circuitry into which C7 is feeding. However, such a fault would almost certainly also have a detrimental effect on the signal at the collector of Tr2, although probably to a much lesser extent. Of course, Tr2 provides a considerable amount of amplification and the signal level at the collector should be far larger than that at the base, and it is necessary to judge whether the signal level detected is roughly correct and not just to confirm that a signal of some sort is present. This can be a little difficult at first, but with practice it will probably become second nature.

Something that should be kept in mind with this circuit is

that the signal at the junction of R6 and R7, and possibly also that at the collector of Tr2 may be very distorted. In fact the signal at the junction of R6 and R7 should be distorted since the signal is clipped at this stage in the circuit. Although severe distortion normally indicates a fault, it does not always do so, and does not in this case. Once again, care must be taken when interpreting results, and it is necessary to reach reasoned conclusions rather than jumping to conclusions. The distortion level at the output of the circuit should be much less as the output filter removes many of the distortion products.

As this chapter has (hopefully) shown, fault finding is a matter of applying a logical and reasoned approach together with a certain amount of technical knowledge. If checks for wiring errors etc. prove fruitless it is a matter of testing the circuit stage by stage using some electronic means until the faulty stages or stages are located.

Chapter 3

COMPONENT TESTING

Voltage tests or checks made using a signal injector/tracer
might lead to a precise diagnosis of the fault, but in most cases
it is necessary to make a few component checks in order to
reach a definite conclusion. Even if voltage checks or other
tests indicate that a certain component is faulty, it is still
necessary to check this component in order to be really sure
that the fault has been correctly diagnosed. In this chapter we
will consider ways of testing the more common components
such as resistors, capacitors, transistors, etc., with the aid of
only a limited amount of test equipment.

Resistors

Testing resistors should give little difficulty since all multimeters seem to cover a reasonably wide resistance measuring
range, and many give quite accurate readings from as little as a
few ohms to many megohms. One point to bear in mind is that
accurate results cannot be guaranteed if the value of a resistor
is measured while it is in circuit unless special equipment is used.
Other resistances in the circuit may shunt the resistance so
that a low reading is obtained even if the resistor is perfectly
satisfactory. If the value indicated is higher than the marked
value of the component then the component is certainly faulty.

As with any two lead component, it is only necessary to
remove one leadout from the circuit board in order to
eliminate the effects of the other components in the circuit.

Capacitors

Capacitors pose more of a problem since few multimers have
capacitance measuring ranges, and some of those that do can
only be used for capacitance measurement in conjunction with
additional equipment which is unlikely to be available to the
user. There are designs for capacitance meters in books and

from time to time in the electronics magazines, and there are also designs for capacitance bridges which are a very simple form of capacitance measuring device.

It is possible to test capacitors to a limited degree using an ordinary multimeter. In theory a capacitor has an infinite resistance between its two leads, and while no practical capacitor achieves this, most capacitors have a resistance that is too high to register on the highest resistance range of a multimeter. A low reading, or even one of a few megohms almost certainly indicates that the component is not usable.

Care must be taken when testing polarised capacitors (such as electrolytic and tantalum types) in this way, since it is essential to connect the multimeter to the capacitor in such a way that the capacitor receives a voltage with the correct polarity. Connecting the multimeter with the wrong polarity would almost certainly result in a reading suggesting that the component was faulty even if it was perfectly satisfactory.

When using a digital multimeter the positive supply comes from the positive test lead, and the negative supply comes from the negative test lead. However, with an analogue instrument the reverse is true, and the negative test lead should be connected to the positive terminal of the capacitor, and the positive test lead should be connected to the negative lead of the capacitor.

Electrolytic capacitors, especially the higher value types, tend to have quite low leakage resistances when compared with other types of capacitor, and a $100\mu F$ electrolytic capacitor for example, may be quite usable even if it has a leakage resistance of only a few hundred kilohms (which many do). This really depends on the proposed application for the component, and a low leakage resistance capacitor is unlikely to prove satisfactory in a critical application such as the timing capacitor in a timer circuit. But a $100\mu F$ capacitor used as a supply decoupling capacitor could easily have a leakage resistance of 100k or even less without causing the circuit to malfunction.

Smaller electrolytic capacitors generally have high leakage resistances of a few megohms at least. Even then there is the possibility of such a component failing to give acceptable results if used in a critical application such as a coupling capacitor between two stages of an amplifier.

When testing a capacitor for leakage you may notice that

initially a quite low reading may be obtained, with the resistance rapidly rising to a very high level. This initial reading is caused by the capacitor charging up to the source voltage of the multimeter, and with a very low value capacitor this effect will probably not be perceptible. On the other hand, with any reasonably large capacitor the reading may well take a few seconds to rise to a high level. With a very large capacitor it could take several minutes for the reading to reach its peak level, although briefly switching the multimeter to a lower resistance measuring range should rapidly charge the capacitor and avoid this long wait.

This initial jump in the meter reading can be used as a way of roughly gauging the value of a capacitor. It will not give a high enough degree of accuracy to show up a capacitor which has a value that is just slightly outside the tolerance limits, and would probably not enable the value of an unmarked capacitor to be reliably established. It is not a method that is usable with very low value capacitors either, since, as mentioned earlier, such capacitors will probably not produce a perceptible initial meter reading. It is also unlikely to work with a digital multimeter. However, with an analogue multimeter and capacitors of more than about 47nF in value (this figure will vary somewhat according to the particular multimeter used) it does give simple "go/no go" testing if no better means are available.

The procedure is to first short circuit the leads of the capacitor to remove any charge it may be storing, and then connect it across the test prods of the meter whilst observing the meter's pointer. Remember to connect the capacitor with the correct polarity if it is a polarised type. You will probably need to use the highest resistance range of the meter except for high value capacitors where it may be necessary to use the range immediately below the highest one. Make a series of tests using capacitors that are known to be operational and make a note of the peak meter reading obtained with each value. This will give you something against which comparisons can be made when testing suspect components.

Diodes

Diodes and rectifiers are the most simple of the semiconductor

54

devices and are the easiest to check. Silicon devices such as the 1N4148, 1N914, 1N4001, etc., should have a very high resistance in one direction and a fairly low resistance in the opposite direction. Germanium devices such as the OA90 and OA91 will also exhibit a low resistance in one direction, but often have a much lower resistance than silicon types in the opposite direction. A resistance of 100k or more should be indicated though.

When using an analogue multimeter the low resistance reading should be obtained when the positive test lead is connected to the cathode (+) leadout wire, and the negative test lead is connected to the anode (−) leadout wire. Reversing the test lead should give a high resistance reading, and there will probably be no perceptible deflection of the meter at all when testing silicon devices. This method of testing is illustrated in Figure 11.

If a digital multimeter is used to test diodes the high and low resistance readings will be the opposite way round to those specified above, and some digital instruments have an inadequate output voltage to test diodes at all.

Note that a diode does not actually have a genuine forward resistance since the voltage drop across the component changes very little with variations in the forward current. Thus the needle deflection will probably change very little as the multimeter is switched from one range to another. It is probably best to initially carry out some checks on a variety of diodes that are known to be functioning correctly, and then you will know what readings to expect when testing a suspect device.

Transistors

There have been numerous transistor checker designs published in electronics books and magazines, and although the increased use of integrated circuits has led to a decrease in the number of transistors to be found in modern electronic circuits, these are still common components and a transistor tester is an extremely useful piece of test equipment. Commercial transistor checkers are also available, and a few multimeters have one built-in.

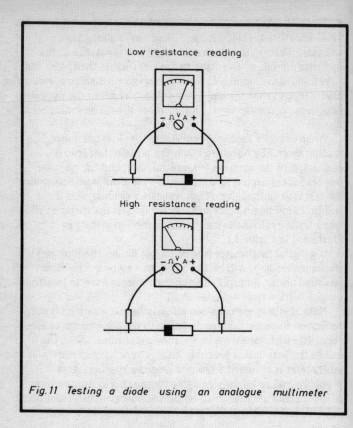

Fig. 11 Testing a diode using an analogue multimeter

It is possible to give transistors a rough check using a multimeter, and the first check is for leakage. If a silicon transistor is fully operational it should provide an extremely high resistance path between its emitter and collector terminals if the base leadout wire is left unconnected, and the supply is connected with the right polarity. Germanium devices tend to have higher leakage levels and can be a little awkward to test, but as they are mostly obsolete and not normally used in new designs this problem is unlikely to arise.

Figure 12 shows the method of connection used for testing NPN transistors, and also the method of connection used for

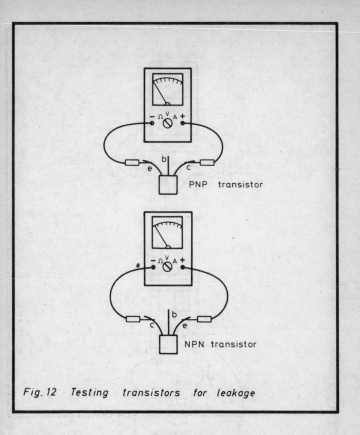

Fig. 12 Testing transistors for leakage

PNP types. Note that in each case the test prods should be connected to the test device with the opposite polarity if a digital multimeter is used. With serviceable silicon devices it is likely that the leakage resistance will often be so high than an ordinary multimeter will be incapable of measuring it.

A rough check of current gain can be made using the arrangement shown in Figure 13. Here the set-up used for leakage testing is repeated, but a resistor has been added between the base and collector terminals of the transistor. For this test it is advisable to use a fairly low resistance range so that the test transistor is operating at a reasonable collector

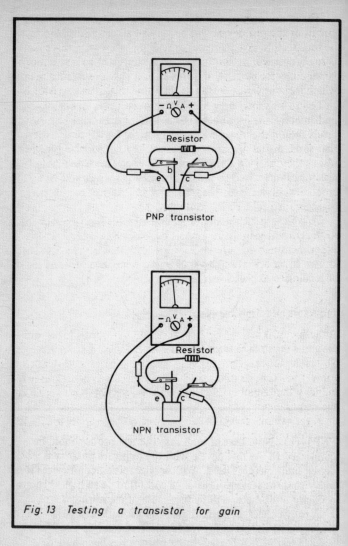

Fig. 13 Testing a transistor for gain

current, and not just a few microamps. The resistor needs to have a value which is roughly equal to the full scale resistance value of the range selected (which will probably be around 10k).

The current which flows through the resistor and the base circuit of the test device will be very small, and should in fact be too small to give a resistance reading. However, this small base current will be amplified by the transistor to give a much larger collector current, and this should give a resistance reading which is significantly less than the value of the bias resistor.

Figure 13 shows how to make this test using an analogue multimeter: it is possible to use a digital instrument but the test prods should then be connected the other way round. Note that some digital multimeters cannot be used for this type of test as they provide an inadequate test voltage. The bias resistor can be wired to the test transistor via a couple of crocodile clip leads, or the transistor and resistor can be wired together on a solderless breadboard.

To some extent the meter reading obtained can be related to the current gain of the transistor under test, and experimenting with a few transistors of various types that are known to be operational will give you some idea of what sort of reading to expect when testing a probable dud.

Inductors and Transformers

An inductor is just a length of wire which is normally wound around a core made from a special material such as ferrite. To test an inductor properly requires an inductance bridge or some other type of inductance measuring equipment, and it is unlikely that amateur electronic enthusiasts will have access to such equipment.

A very simple test that can be done quite easily is to check for a low resistance through the component. In theory an inductance has zero resistance, but in practice many high value RF types have resistances of a few ten of ohms, or even a few hundred ohms. On the other hand, high current, low value audio types may have a resistance of less than an ohm. Often retailers or manufacturers data will specify the resistance for the component in question, although it might not always be possible to track down this information.

The importance of knowing the proper resistance of an inductor is simply that the fact that there is continuity through an inductor does not necessarily mean that the component is fully functional. The most common cause of problems with inductors is the wire either breaking or burning out so that there is no DC path through the component. This is not the only problem though, and damage to the wire's insulation can result in some of the turns in the coil becoming short circuited. RF chokes are sometimes wound using Litz wire (a form of multistrand wire), and a fault that can occur with these is some of the strands becoming broken while the others remain intact.

If the approximate (correct) resistance for the inductor is known, shorted turns may be indicated by a suspiciously low resistance reading, and broken strands should certainly give a higher than expected resistance reading.

Transformers are even more difficult to comprehensively test than inductors, and it is again really just a case of measuring the resistance through each winding to check for broken or burnt out wires, or for short circuited windings. Unfortunately, in most cases it will not be possible to find out exactly what resistance readings should be obtained when testing a transformer. When dealing with audio types (which are little used these days) do not confuse impedance figures with the resistances through the windings. The resistance is generally only a small fraction of the impedance.

With the mains transformers, which are about the only type of transformer in common use in amateur electronic designs at present, it is obviously possible to test the component while it is in the project and the power is switched on. If the correct voltage is present across the primary winding of the component, and the correct output voltages are not present, then the component is almost certainly faulty. Any resistance checks on the component when it has been removed from the project are really just done to confirm what is already known. One point to bear in mind when testing a mains transformer while it is operating is that the secondary windings must be disconnected before it can be definitely decided that the transformer is faulty since the problem might otherwise be due to an overload causing little or no output voltage.

Of course, when making measurements on a mains transform it is necessary to take great care not to touch any of the mains wiring so that dangerous electric shocks are avoided. Also be careful not to accidentally short circuit one of the mains tags of the transformer to any other part of the circuit.

Op Amps

Testing most integrated circuits is rather difficult, and in most cases it is a matter of checking all the circuitry around the device, and if this all seems to be correct then it is reasonable to assume that the integrated circuit is faulty. With some of the more simple devices it is possible to construct a simple test circuit, and an example of the type of integrated circuit that can be checked in this way is the operational amplifier.

A simple test circuit for operational amplifiers is shown in Figure 14, and as this type of integrated circuit is so popular you may consider it to be worthwhile constructing this circuit as a proper piece of test equipment. This is not really necessary though if you own a solderless breadboard since with the aid of

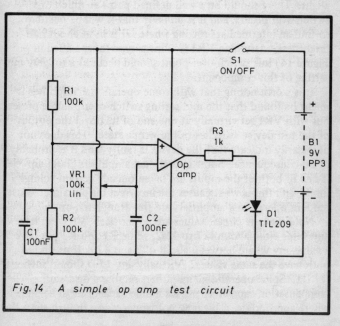

Fig. 14   A simple op amp test circuit

one of these it is a very easy matter to quickly build up this test circuit when it is required.

R1 and R2 bias the non-inverting (+) input of the device to half the supply voltage, and C1 decouples any stray feedback to this input which might otherwise cause instability. VR1 is used to supply an adjustable bias voltage to the inverting (−) input, and C2 decouples any stray feedback to this input. D1 is a LED indicator which enables the output stage of the test device to be monitored, and R3 is a current limiting resistor.

With VR1 adjusted for a low voltage at the inverting input the output of the test device should go high and D1 should light up quite brightly. As VR1 is adjusted for increased slider voltage a point will be reached where the voltage fed to the inverting input of the test device is higher than that fed to the non-inverting input, and at this point D1 should switch off. In fact many operational amplifiers have a minimum output voltage of about 2.5 volts, and as the forward threshold voltage of most LEDs is about 1.8 volts this will still leave D1 dimly alight. There should be a well defined point at which this switch-over occurs, and it is unlikely that it will be possible to find an intermediate setting where D1 is lit at about half brightness. Assuming VR1 is a linear type (as specified in Figure 14) this switch-over point should occur at a roughly mid setting of this component.

It is worth noting that with some operational amplifiers it might be found that the mid setting switch-over point is present, but with VR1 set virtually at one end of its travel the output of the test device switches to the wrong state. This does not necessarily indicate that the device is faulty, and it is probably of no consequence. Some operational amplifiers "latch-up" if one or both of the inputs are taken outside certain voltage limits, and this is what causes the incorrect output state. Most modern operational amplifiers are free from latch-up.

Note that the circuit values are not critical. VR1 can have any value from about 4k7 to 2M2, while R1 and R2 can have a value any where between about 4k7 and 470k (but should both have the same value). Virtually any LED should suffice for D1. Some operational amplifiers require a discrete compensation capacitor, and a suitable capacitor can be added where appropriate. This may not be necessary though since the operational amplifier under test is used open loop, and may well be sufficiently stable without a compensation capacitor.

SCRs

A silicon controlled rectifier (SCR or thyristor) is a simple switching device which can be tested using the test circuit shown in Figure 15. Once again, this could be made as a permanent unit, but it would probably be better just to breadboard the circuit when it is needed.

With a supply of the correct polarity, a thyristor can be made to conduct between its anode and cathode terminals by applying a forward bias to the gate terminal. The bias required to trigger the device to the conductive state varies considerably from one device to another, but is usually under 20mA. By operating S1 the test device can be given a forward gate bias of about 20mA, and should therefore be triggered into conduction so that LED indicator D1 lights up.

A thyristor will hold-on once it has been triggered if an anode to cathode current of about 20mA or more is passed by the device. In this circuit the test device passes a suitably high

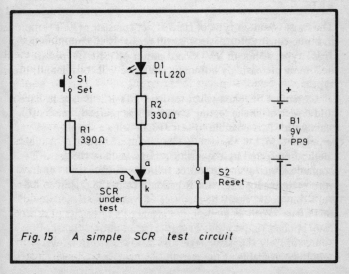

Fig. 15   A simple SCR test circuit

current and D1 should therefore remain switched on once S1 has been released. An SCR can be switched off by briefly taking the anode to cathode current below the hold-on current, and this can be achieved here by briefly operating S2 so that the LED current is diverted through this switch and away from the thyristor. Thus D1 should switch off when S2 is released.

Triacs can be tested in the same way, but these devices can operate using a supply of either polarity, and the same circuit action should be obtained even if the supply polarity is reversed. Some triacs have a built-in diac in series with the gate, and these cannot be tested using the circuit of Figure 15. These devices can in fact be rather difficult to test, and it is really another example where it is necessary to check all the other circuitry, and assume the device is faulty if the other circuitry appears to be satisfactory.

Diacs are similarly difficult to test, but should not conduct in either direction when tested with an ordinary multimeter or continuity tester (which will give inadequate voltage to trigger these devices).

FETs

The most common type of field effect transistor (FET) employed in home-constructor designs is still probably the junction or JFET type, although VMOS and power MOSFET types are becoming increasingly common. Here we will consider all three types.

Care must be taken when testing FETs as it is easy to have a dud device after the testing even if it was perfectly serviceable to start with! It is possible to test JFETs using a simple dual supply set-up, but the simple test circuit of Figure 16 is the method preferred by the author. Here we have the test FET connected into a simple source follower buffer stage. The voltage across load resistor R3 should be in the region of 4.5 volts, but could easily be a couple of volts or so either side of this figure. With an audio input signal of a few volts peak to peak applied to the input of this stage an output signal of approximately the same level and of low distortion level should be available at the output.

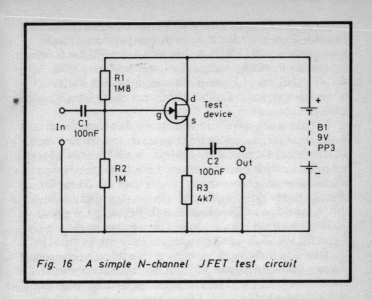

Fig. 16   A simple N-channel JFET test circuit

This is another test circuit that can be breadboarded when required, and it is probably not worthwhile constructing it as a permanent piece of test gear. The output signal can be monitored using a signal tracer such as the one described earlier in this book, an amplifier and loudspeaker, or simply using a crystal earphone. An input signal can be obtained from a sinewave generator, or the audio output from the earphone socket of a cassette recorder or transistor radio can be used.

Note that this test circuit is for an N channel JFET, but it will also work with a P channel type if the supply polarity is reversed.

VMOS transistors are more like bipolar transistors than JFETs in many respects, and they are devices which are normally switched off and need a forward bias to bring them into conduction. A characteristic which they do have in common with JFETs is that they are voltage operated and have an extremely high input impedance, unlike bipolar devices which have a significant input current requirement and fairly low input impedance.

The method of testing bipolar transistors described earlier

65

in this book may work with VMOS devices, but many multimeters will not provide a high enough output voltage to give satisfactory results (VMOS devices tend to have higher forward conduction threshold voltages than bipolar devices). The simple test circuit of Figure 17 can be used to test VMOS devices though, and is another circuit that can be breadboarded when it is required.

With the slider of VR1 at the bottom of its track the test device is cut off, no significant drain current should flow, and LED indicator D1 should not light up. If VR1 is adjusted for a steadily increasing slider voltage a point should soon be reached where the test transistor begins to switch on and D1 starts to visibly glow. Taking the wiper voltage slightly above this threshold point should result in D1 lighting up brightly.

This test circuit is for N channel devices, but there are a few P channel VMOS devices available, and these can be tested in the same way if the supply polarity is reversed. The component values are not critical, and VR1 can have a value anywhere between 4k7 and 2M2. D1 can be any LED having an output in the visible spectrum, and R1 can have a value of anywhere between about 470k and 10M. R2 should not be changed

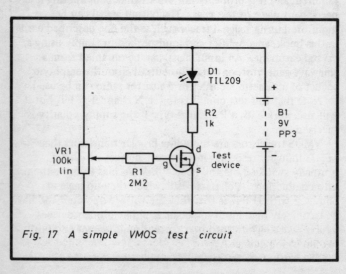

Fig. 17 A simple VMOS test circuit

significantly in value as this could result in an inadequate or
excessive LED current.

Power MOSFET devices can be tested using the same
circuit, but note that manufacturers of these devices
recommend that a short gate lead should be used in order to
avoid instability and possible damage to the test device. It is
obviously necessary to observe the normal MOS handling
precautions when dealing with a VMOS or power MOSFET
device that does not have integral protection circuitry.

Unijunctions

Unijunctions have little in common with bipolar transistors, and
need to be tested in a totally different fashion. A unijunction
transistor is analagous to the circuit shown in Figure 18, and it
is possible using resistance checks to ensure that the appropriate
approximate resistance is present between the base 1 and base
2 terminals, and that a diode action is present between the
emitter terminal and either of the bases.

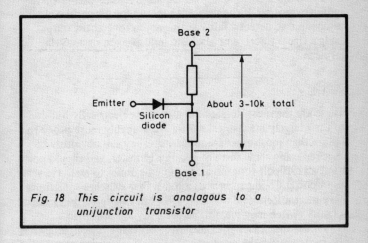

Fig. 18 This circuit is analagous to a
unijunction transistor

A more reliable check for unijunction transistors is to use the
simple test circuit of Figure 19. Here the device under test is
connected in a simple relaxation oscillator operating at an

67

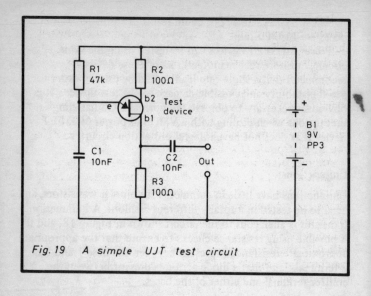

Fig. 19   A simple UJT test circuit

audio frequency. If the device is functioning properly it should be possible to detect a fairly strong audio tone at the output using a signal tracer, amplifier and loudspeaker, or a crystal earpiece.

Switches

These are the most simple of components electrically but due to their largely mechanical nature are probably more prone to failure than most other components. They can obviously be checked using some form of continuity tester, and should not be at all difficult for even a complete beginner to test. However, an important point to bear in mind is that switches sometimes have intermittent faults so that after carrying out a quick check a faulty switch may seem to be perfectly alright. Also remember that a lack of continuity between two contacts with the switch set to the appropriate position is not the only fault that can occur, and it is possible (although admittedly rare) for a switch to produce an electrical contact between two tags when it should not.

It is therefore advisable to connect the continuity tester between the appropriate two tags and then adjust the switch through its full number of positions a few times to see if continuity is always indicated at only the correct times.

Switches that have numerous tags are often the cause of mistakes in the wiring due to the constructor misinterpreting which tag is which. Before wiring up a switch, especially if it is a type you are unfamiliar with, examine the component carefully and if necessary use a continuity tester to check that you are interpreting the tags correctly.

Another point to watch is that although you may be using a switch which looks similar to the one illustrated in a wiring diagram, it may in fact use a different contact arrangement! This is also a problem that can occur with some types of socket and is possible with certain other types of component. It is a good idea to check points unless you are using components with which you are familiar, as this can save a lot of time searching for a simple fault that need never have occured in the first place.

Chapter 4

LOGIC CIRCUITS

In many respects fault-finding on digital equipment is the same
as for linear circuits, but there are a few fairly obvious and
important differences. Primarily the difference is that in digital
circuits there are only two signal levels; logic 1 (high or close to
the positive supply voltage) and logic 0 (low or close to the
negative supply voltage). Some devices also have a third state
where the output is effectively disconnected from the
appropriate terminal of the device, but in such cases a floating
output should be taken to one or other of the two normal logic
states by the output of another device. With only two signal
levels to contend with the problem of fault-finding is made
very much easier.

What actually constitutes the high and low logic states
depends on the particular logic family in use, and in some cases
it is also dependent on the supply voltage used. The popular
TTL logic integrated circuits (which are intended to operate on
a nominal 5 volt supply) require a low logic level to be 0.8
volts or less, and a high logic level to be 2 volts or more. Things
are less straight forward with CMOS devices which can operate
over a supply voltage range of about 3 to 20 volts, and the
minimum acceptable voltage for logic 1 varies with the supply
voltage used (as does the maximum acceptable logic 0 voltage).
However, logic 0 should be about 30% of the supply voltage
or less, and logic 1 should be approximately 70% of the supply
potential or more. Unless the output of a CMOS IC is loaded
quite heavily, by a LED indicator for example, the output
potential is actually likely to be within a few millivolts of the
appropriate supply line.

Testing voltages in a logic circuit is likely to lead to
incorrect conclusions due to the nature of signals in logic
circuits. Testing the output of a CMOS logic device might
reveal a voltage reading of about half the supply voltage, and
it might seem reasonable to assume from this that the output
is between the two logic levels and that the device is therefore

faulty. This might not be the case, and it could simply be that
the output is rapidly switching backwards and forwards from
one logic level to the other, and that the multimeter is
reading the average voltage of about half the supply voltage as it
could not respond fast enough to follow the changing voltage
level.

One way around this is to check logic circuits using an
oscilloscope which will clearly show if the input is a static
voltage or one that is pulsing. It will also show the waveshape
of the signal if desired. A simple alternative to this is a logic
probe, and there are many published designs for these in
addition to a number of ready-made units which can be
obtained from some of the larger component retailers. These
usually have a number of LED indicators to show the logic
state at the test point, with perhaps four LEDs to indicate
logic 1, logic 0, a static input between the logic levels, and a
pulsing input. To be of real value, in the author's opinion at
any rate, a logic probe should be able to differentiate between
a pulsing signal and a static level between the logic states. It is
not actually any better than a multimeter if it cannot do so.

With the more complex logic circuits it can be very useful
to be able to monitor a number of points in the circuit
simultaneously. Home-constructor designs for pieces of test
equipment of this type are described in magazines from time
to time, and commercially produced equipment for this type of
monitoring is available. There is probably no point in having
fairly advanced logic testing equipment of this kind unless you
build a lot of the more complex digital projects, and for simple
projects or only the occasional complex logic circuit a logic
probe should be perfectly adequate.

Pulse Generator

When testing digital circuits it is sometimes possible to use a
technique that is analagous to feeding an input signal into a
piece of audio equipment and then using a signal tracer to
check the signal present at strategic points in the circuit.
However, when testing digital circuits the input signal is
provided either by a pulse generator or the internal clock of
the circuit, or possible by both. The signal is monitored using

71

an oscilloscope or some form of logic probe. Using a pulse generator running at a low frequency it is in fact often possible to use an ordinary multimeter to check the logic levels present in the circuit since there will be no high frequency signals to give misleading results. Testing many logic devices is more convenient at low speed anyway, especially if only basic test equipment is available.

Pulse generators can be, and often are, quite complex pieces of equipment, but for normal amateur use a simple device is usually perfectly adequate and a more viable proposition. The simple pulse generator design to be described here is one that I have found to be very useful even though it is based on a single integrated circuit and employs few other components. The unit has "high" and "low" output times that are independent of one another, both having four switched times of 1, 10, 100 and 1000 milliseconds. Thus the unit can provide a 0.5Hz squarewave, brief positive or negative pulses at one second intervals, and can also give a high output frequency (e.g. a 500Hz squarewave if both output times are set at 1 millisecond) if required. The availability of a higher output frequency is useful when testing a divider chain where a very low input frequency may necessitate a wait of many seconds of even minutes before any change in output state could be expected.

The Circuit

The circuit diagram of the pulse generator is given in Figure 20(a), and as can be seen from this the integrated circuit used in the unit is an ICM7555 which is the CMOS version of the popular 555 timer device. Although the ICM7555 is a CMOS device it is capable of driving TTL and other families of logic devices, and the unit is not restricted to use with CMOS circuits. The unit does not have its own power supply, and uses the supply of the circuit under investigation. The current consumption of the unit is only around 100 microamps (plus any output current that flows) and this method should not therefore cause any problems.

The circuit is a form of astable, but is not the standard 555 type which is outlined in Figure 20(b). This operates by having C_a first charge to two thirds of the supply voltage via R_a and

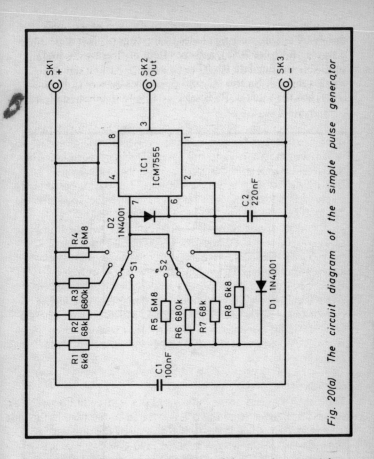

Fig. 20(a) The circuit diagram of the simple pulse generator

Rb, and then discharge to one third of the supply potential through Rb and a low impedance path provided by an internal transistor of the ICM7555. Ca then charges up to two thirds of the supply voltage again, and so on. The output goes high while Ca is charging and low while it is discharging. Since the charge resistance for Ca must always be larger than the discharge resistance this configuration must have a high output time which is longer than the low output time.

Although there seems to be a general belief that this has to be the case with a 555 astable circuit, it is in fact possible to

73

make the low output time longer than the high output period simply by adding steering diodes to the circuit. This method is shown in Figure 20(b), and the effect of steering diodes D1 and D2 is to eliminate Rb from Ca's charge path. Ca now charges through Ra and D2, and discharges by way of Rb and D1. Thus the value of Ra is selected to give the desired high

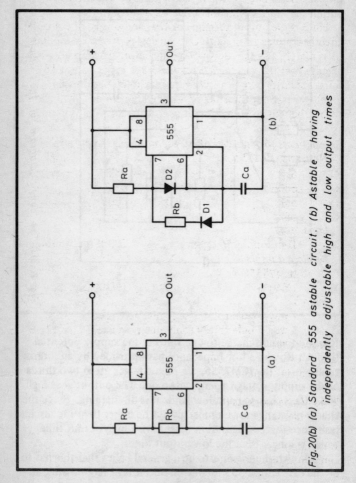

Fig.20(b) (a) Standard 555 astable circuit. (b) Astable having independently adjustable high and low output times

output period and Rb has a value which gives the required low output time. In both cases the output period is approximately equal to 0.69 CR seconds.

Returning to the circuit diagram of Figure 20(a), the high output period is determined by whichever of the four resistors (R1 to R4) is selected using S1. R1 to R4 give nominal output times of 1, 10, 100 and 1000 milliseconds respectively using the specified value for timing capacitor C2. The same low output periods are available using S2 and R5 to R8.

Pin 3 is the output terminal of IC1, and this is, of course, directly coupled to the input of the device driven by the unit. C1 is merely a supply decoupling capacitor. The circuit will operate over the very wide supply voltage range of 2 to 18 volts; the latter being the absolute maximum permissible supply voltage for the ICM7555 integrated circuit. This should enable the unit to be used with practically any logic circuit.

Components for Simple Pulse Generator (Figure 20(a))
   Resistors, all 1/3 watt 5%

R1	6k8	R2	68k
R3	680k	R4	6M8
R5	6M8	R6	680k
R7	68k	R8	6k8

   Capacitors

C1	100nF polyester	C2	220nF polycarbonate

   Semiconductors

IC1	ICM7555		
D1	1N4001	D2	1N4001

   Switches

S1   4 way 3 pole rotary (only one pole used)
S2   4 way 3 pole rotary (only one pole used)
   Miscellaneous
Case
0.1in matrix stripboard
Two control knobs
Three wander sockets (SK1–SK3)
Wire, solder, etc.

Construction
Some of the components are fitted onto a 0.1in matrix

stripboard; 11 strips by 13 holes, and the component layout and other details of the component panel are provided in Figure 21. The board is constructed in the usual way, and although the ICM7555 is a CMOS device it does not require any special handling precautions as it has very effective internal protection circuitry.

The eight resistors are mounted direct on S1 and S2, as can be seen from Figure 21 which details all the wiring of the unit in addition to illustrating the component panel. It will probably be necessary to cut the leadout wires of the resistors quite short as they might otherwise protrude too far back into the case (although this obviously depends on the case and general layout adopted for the unit). If the leadout wires are cut quite short be sure to only apply the soldering iron quite briefly to each resistor as it is soldered into place, so that they do not become overheated with a consequent loss of accuracy. They will be more easily soldered into place if the ends of their leadout wires and the relevant tags of S1 and S2 are generously tinned with solder first.

Using the Unit

In use the unit is coupled to the supply of the equipment under test by way of a pair of test leads having wander plugs that connect to the pulse generator and crocodile clips which connect to the equipment under test at suitable and convenient points. It is a good idea to use leads, plugs, sockets and clips of different colours for each supply connection so that the risk of getting the supply polarity wrong is minimised (the ICM7555 may well be damaged if the supply polarity should be incorrect).

The output of the unit is coupled to the test circuit via an ordinary test lead having a wander plug at one end and a test prod at the other. Be careful only to apply the output of the unit to the inputs of logic devices, and not to outputs or a high current could flow from IC1 causing damage to the circuit under investigation. It may sometimes be necessary to remove an integrated circuit from the unit being tested so that the pulse generator can drive an input without also driving the output that normally feeds into that input. There will not normally be any difficulty here since this will probably just entail unplugging

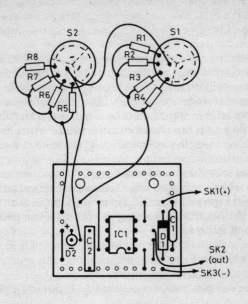

Fig. 21 Constructional details of the simple pulse generator

the integrated circuit from its holder, although appropriate care must obviously be exercised when dealing with MOS devices, especially the more expensive types.

Logic ICs

When dealing with logic circuits it is very useful to have some technical knowledge of the integrated circuits used in the projects you construct. Many digital circuits consist of a number of logic devices and very little else apart from a mass of printed circuit tracks! Without a reasonable knowledge of the devices employed in the circuit it will be difficult to fault-find unless a simple mechanical fault is located, or a logic probe shows up an obvious fault.

Gates are mostly quite easy to test, and what are called "truth tables" are useful when testing these. The truth table shown in Figure 22 is for a 2 input NAND type, and this simply shows the output state for various input state combinations. Using this in conjunction with a logic probe or some other form of logic tester it should obviously be possible to quickly check whether or not the appropriate output is produced for the given set of input conditions.

More complex logic devices can be a little more difficult to

Input 1	Input 2	Output
LOW	LOW	HIGH
LOW	HIGH	HIGH
HIGH	LOW	HIGH
HIGH	HIGH	LOW

Fig. 22 The truth table for a positive 2 input NAND gate

78

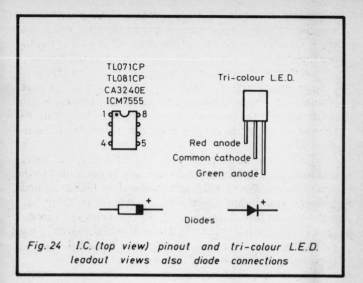

TL071CP
TL081CP
CA3240E
ICM7555

Tri-colour L.E.D.

Red anode
Common cathode
Green anode

Diodes

*Fig. 24   I.C. (top view) pinout and tri-colour L.E.D.
leadout views also diode connections*

Notes

Please note overleaf is a list of other titles that are available in our range of Radio, Electronics and Computer Books.

These should be available from all good Booksellers, Radio Component Dealers and Mail Order Companies.

However, should you experience difficulty in obtaining any title in your area, then please write directly to the publisher enclosing payment to cover the cost of the book plus adequate postage.

If you would like a complete catalogue of our entire range of Radio, Electronics and Computer Books then please send a Stamped Addressed Envelope to:

BERNARD BABANI (publishing) LTD
THE GRAMPIANS
SHEPHERDS BUSH ROAD
LONDON W6 7NF
ENGLAND